Gentle Birth Companions:

Doulas Serving Humanity

Adela Stockton

2010

Published in 2010 by
McCubbington Press
Auldgirth
Dumfries DG2 0JX
www.adelastockton.co.uk

The Author has made every effort to ensure the accuracy of the information presented in this book. However, the Author cannot accept responsibility for any accident, injury or loss resulting from the use of this book. Medical advice and personal judgement should be considered when making any decisions about care during the childbearing year.

ISBN 978-1-907931-00-0

Edited by Maddie McMahon
Cover Art by Marlene L'Abbe, Water Spider Designs
Designed and Printed by Solway Offset, Dumfries, Scotland

"As you listen, do not seek solutions. Just wait in silence. You will gain strength and greater understanding."

Sheila Kitzinger, 2006 p.151[1]

Dedicated to Daz the doula

'Adela Stockton engages the reader with this thoughtful, accessible and well-researched account of the doula movement: its evolution, its current form, and its possible future role in birth care provision. A book like this is long overdue, and should be required reading for anyone interested in supporting women during the childbearing year.'
Leah Hazard, doula and author of *The Father's Home Birth Handbook.*

'Thank you Adela for a lively historical journey through the new and yet ageless doula movement; a beautiful, subtle and accurate description of what a doula is really about. This book is a must for all would-be doulas and for future parents seeking that special 'tender loving support' around childbirth that is desperately missing nowadays.'
Valérie Dupin, Co-Présidente de *l'Association Doulas de France.*

CONTENTS

Foreword by Vida Rye

Back in the year 2000, many doors were still closed to doulas in the UK. Yet I knew instinctively that the role of the doula was going to be an important one, so I bought the domain name *www.doula.org.uk*. Fortunately, there were others that felt the same excitement as me and barely a year later, the first gathering of UK doulas took place at Michel Odent's house in London. I had no real comprehension then that the website I had created would become such a great resource for communication between doulas all around the UK. It put me in contact with many wonderful women who were already doula-ing or about to embark on their doula journey, and this is how I met Adela Stockton, doula, doula course provider, former midwife, author and devoted mum, from Scotland.

Before I met Adela, I had trained with the not-for-profit *Holloway Doula Group* (now *Birth Companions*) and had been working in the community too. My doula inspirations were the likes of Pam Adams, Liliana Lammers, Ingrid Lewis and Pauline Armstrong, who I met at the first meetings of our UK doula network. These exceptional women did not need 'training', their innate wisdom and life experience oozed from them in a gentle, loving and yet powerful way to the younger, more inexperienced doulas around them. Pam in particular was very encouraging and could write about what I felt it was to be a doula when I was often unable to articulate it for myself.

In those early days of *Doula UK* (then known as the *Independent Doula Association*) I worked closely with Pam producing the newsletter and mailing it out to the ever-growing membership. I loved Pam's reflections, such as: *"I think that the people who teach us most about our job are our clients. We learn from experience. Being a doula is like being an artist, each woman brings to her job her innate talents, her personal skill, genuineness and experience. No two doulas will work in the same way because no two families are the same. So in answer to the question, "What do doulas do?", they adapt their personalities and nurturing skills to meet the needs of their individual clients and the clients' unique situations."*

We wanted to be transparent in our dealings with each other and the wider community. We did not want to create 'levels' or hierarchies or to found the network on a fear-based philosophy (like some of the births at which we supported). I asked if, instead of 'Training', we could use the term 'Doula Journey', and again, Pam put this idea into words for us, words which you can still read on the *Doula UK* website under "Journey to being a doula". Pam was also prepared to speak out about what others may have been too afraid to say, to open up discussion amongst the network. As she said: *"Doulas come from many walks of life and we share a common belief in the importance of "being there" for the mothers we serve. But already we are discovering that there are interesting and varied approaches to many of the issues surrounding birth and infant and child care..."*

There were many lengthy discussions about such topics as: "Do we want to adopt the term 'doula'?" "Can you be a doula, when you are not a mother?" "Can there be male doulas?" "Do we want to be a 'profession'?" "Does a doula have to be 'trained'?" If so, "What is training then?"

I continued to work with and for *Doula UK* for a few years after moving to New Zealand in 2002. Since finally hanging up my *DUK* hat, it has been amazing to see the hard work continuing, in striving to grow the network and provide strong encouragement and support for doulas. However, it has also been interesting to have watched from afar, the struggle as prescription and 'corporateness' seems to have crept in somewhat, although I realise that this may in part be a reflection of what society is demanding of doulas.

I did not believe when coming to New Zealand that I would have a doula role because I had heard what a fantastic maternity system was in place, with autonomy for midwives and continuity of care and carer. Indeed, I feel very privileged to have home birthed my own two girls here with incredible midwives. However, I have lately witnessed how one-to-one care is being eroded and birth becoming more medicalised, just as in the Netherlands. Now, in 2010, there is a touch of déjà vu for me as we begin to talk about the idea of a network for doulas in New Zealand, and similar discussions are cropping up to those we had 10 years ago, in the UK.

Doula care is based upon the belief that pregnancy, labour and birth are more than just physiological processes, they are psychosocial too, and this is why it is valuable for doulas to be included in the maternity care arena. They can work alongside midwives and the medical community, to respectfully encourage women to take more proactive responsibility in their own care. I believe that no limit can be set on the love and nurturing offered to a woman in her birthing years. Mothers and fathers need to be exposed to all the options of conscious birthing and conscious parenting, so they can make informed choices of where and with whom they birth and what follows after birth.

I have never wanted the introduction of doulas to build bureaucracy or another layer of professionalism in an already overcrowded maternity system, as this just destroys both trust and autonomy. I believe it is vitally important to remain as lay women, transparent about what we individually bring to our role as doulas, whilst continuing an open and ongoing education and reflection.

I feel so honoured, therefore, to have been invited to write this Foreword for Adela's new book, and it gives me great pleasure to say that *Gentle Birth Companions* is the doula book that I have been waiting for, for over a decade. It is essential reading for everyone wanting to know about, or become a doula; I extend my warmest thanks to Adela for writing so clearly about the origins of the lay childbirth companion and about what it is to really be a doula.

Sincere thanks too, for Adela's clear tribute to all the many midwives across the world who provide outstanding care. I will be particularly encouraging the midwives within my community to read this book, to facilitate their understanding of how the doula comes from a nurturing and positive place, that she is not someone to fear. I anticipate that *Gentle Birth Companions* will open further doors for doulas, enabling them to work respectfully alongside maternity carers in providing wholesome support for women and their families during the childbirth year.

Vida Rye, mother of two home birthed baby girls, a founding member of Doula UK, former member and trustee of Birth Companions and currently a calmbirth® practitioner in New Zealand. September, 2010

Introduction

'doula': *lay companion to birthing families*
'social support': *emotional and practical assistance*

It is easy to imagine, when you are immersed, as I am, in the natural birth world, that everyone knows about doulas. Yet I have only to step outside my bubble for a moment, to soon find myself explaining to people, yet again, that I am neither a 'jeweller' nor a 'dealer' - followed by a swift synopsis of exactly how the doula role differs from that of the midwife.

While my interest lies in encouraging mothers and fathers to protect the gentle birth of their baby and to secure the kind of care and support that is needed to enable them to do this, I am not concerned so much with who provides this support, more that it is delivered in a way that feels right for the parents. Increasingly, as health professionals' clinical workloads intensify, often meaning less time to provide psychosocial support, I find that members of the community are stepping up to this role instead.

So it was partly driven by the desire to share more widely the extraordinary - and still largely unknown - benefits of lay support for mothers and fathers during pregnancy, birth and early parenting, that I set out to write this book. The other part of me felt that, as no text covering the UK and European doula movement yet existed, it was time that the doula communities among countries beyond the US had a voice.

Formerly an NHS midwife, I have worked as a doula since 2002. As well as supporting mothers and couples during their time around childbirth, I act as doula to new doulas coming through my Mindful Doulas course (Birth Consultancy). I have been a volunteer for national network Doula UK since 2002 (currently Joint Assessor/Mentor Co-ordinator) and in 2007, I was instrumental in formally establishing the peer support group Scottish Doula Network. I am fortunate to have been able to build on and develop, on a continuing basis, what I have instinctively always known about protecting physiological birth and supporting early parenting, through my work as a lay supporter.

Through examining the emergence of the doula and exploring the significance of her continuing role, the intention of this book is to tell the story of the 'doula movement', particularly focusing on the UK and Europe, where it is about to enter the second decade of its existence. Divided into three parts, the first section explores the whats, whys and wherefores of the doula. Who she is, where she comes from, what she does, what training she needs, if any; and it is here that the role and activities of doula networks around the UK, Europe and beyond are outlined. The second part of the book looks at why birthing families need social support and, in the light of recent evidence, how this is provided by doulas, whether during pregnancy, birth or the postnatal period. How the doula works in relation to midwives and the provision of maternity care services, including the idea of doula-ing as a stepping-stone towards the revival of traditional midwifery, are also examined. The final section of the book contains a selection of inspiring vignettes contributed by working doulas, including birth and postnatal stories and personal doula journeys.

It is my hope that *Gentle Birth Companions* serves to inform the reader about the value of lay support during childbirth, and to clarify any myths or misconceptions about the modern doula's role in countries beyond the US, from where the idea originated. This book provides essential reading for anyone considering becoming a doula, as well as both novice and experienced doulas; in addition, it is a key reference for midwives, student midwives, obstetricians, birth educators and others working in the field of childbirth. My sincere hope is that it also serves to assist pregnant women, new mothers, fathers and families, in securing appropriately sensitive support for themselves around the time that their baby is born.

Part One - GRASSROOTS

'support': be present and give encouragement, give assistance/comfort, care for
'intervene': become involved in a situation, have a preventive or delaying effect

1. Origins of the doula

Womanly support

"When a woman went into labour they would gather in the red tent and share their wisdom from their own births. They would sing songs of encouragement, calling on the goddesses who give strength, feeding the labouring woman morsels of honey and nutrient rich cakes and fruit to keep her energies up. They would rub her feet and hands with fragrant oils. All the while trusting in the wisdom of her body to know how to expel the baby."

Maria Sterrenberg, 2006[1]

The tradition of women supporting other women during the time around childbirth, whether as a female relative, friend, neighbour, trusted servant or as a midwife, has been honoured since ancient times.[2] With her unique status as someone who possesses specialist knowledge and skills in the necessary care and intervention during pregnancy, birth and the postnatal period, the midwife's role has long been recognised and valued.[3] Yet equally, the significance of the additional support provided by lay (untrained) people close to the birthing family is not to be underestimated. Any woman's experience of giving birth and mothering can be, has been, and still is, positively applied to assist and support another mother, woman to woman, sister to sister, mother to mother.[4, 5]

However, widespread erosion of local community in the modern industrialised world has resulted in less availability of sustained social support from the mother-to-be's family and friends. With the progressive fragmentation and medicalisation of care during childbirth, there are now over two generations of women who have had predominantly interventional and traumatic experiences of birth, with poor histories of breastfeeding. How willing, or indeed able, are these (grand)mothers to support their daughters to give birth without fear? How effectively can new mothers gain confidence in breastfeeding, nurturing and building on their new role, without experienced family members or community around them?

Described as a lay companion who usually has personal experience of birth and mothering herself, a new supportive figure has emerged in the field of childbirth, namely the doula. Additionally, she has usually undertaken a basic course of learning in preparation for her role. Where a female relative or friend is not available, emotionally or physically, to support the expectant woman or new mother and her partner, the doula is hired by the parents to stand in as an alternative. The fact that she has the experience and skills to do this may set her at a different starting point to a family member, friend or neighbour, yet it does not mean that she is trained or qualified to replace the midwife. So who exactly is the doula?

In order to get a feel for where the contemporary doula may have originated, we can explore potential archetypes for her role dating as far back as the Ancient Egyptian era (c.3150-31 BC). However, so as not to confuse the doula's role with that of the traditional lay midwife, let us begin by briefly outlining the origins of the midwife herself. In this way we can attempt to clarify the inherent *differences* between the two roles, an essential component to the overall understanding of this book.

Ancient Birth Attendants: 'with woman' or 'wise woman'?

Although the actual word 'midwife', created from the Old English to mean 'with woman', did not exist in the English language until c.1300 AD,[6] the existence of a female figure attributed with possessing unique qualities and skills in the art and science of supporting childbirth, to whom the term 'midwife' has been applied in translation, can be traced back to biblical times. 'Midwives' are mentioned in the Old Testament (c.1800 BC),[7-8] derived from the ancient Hebrew word 'to beget' or 'to bear', which in turn meant someone who 'causes or helps to bring forth.'[9]

The role of the ancient midwife was fundamentally to provide social support, yet she also possessed the physical skills and spiritual connections to intervene in the birth process as she saw necessary. She could massage the womb and the cervix to aid the action of the muscles, she would prepare and implement herbs to ease the passage of birth and she assisted in the management of the placenta and care of the baby's cord. She would also call upon the gods and spirits through prayer and song to protect the mother on her journey through birth and to welcome the new baby. She was both 'with woman' and 'wise woman'.[10] Records suggest that the early midwives learned their skills through apprenticeship and that this route to qualification was sustained through Roman times (27 BC–AD 1453), when novice midwives rose from the slave classes to acquire their freedom in return for the services they provided. During the Ancient Greek era (c.1100-146 BC), formalised academic midwifery training was initiated where a standard of literacy was required of all students. It appears that by around the advent of Christianity, the distinction between the professional midwife ('with woman'), who charged for her services, and the lay midwife ('wise woman'), who continued to serve mothers within the poorer communities, had been established.[11]

This socio-economic division in the provision of midwifery care continued to exist through the ages. Licensing for midwives was introduced in Europe (c.1550-1750), England (1902), Scotland (1915) and America (1920s), in efforts to outlaw what was considered to be the poorer practice of the 'unsworn' midwife, 'granny' or 'handy' woman, or 'howdie'.[12, 13, 14, 15] These lay midwives, who already enjoyed something of a 'community companion' standing within their local area, continued to practice regardless, providing social support as an integral part of their care, although in some cases the 'sworn' or 'licensed' midwife was called upon if a birth developed complications.[16] Even today, the roles of the qualified, regulated midwife, commonly affiliated to industrialised areas, and the untrained, unregulated midwife or Traditional Birth Attendant (TBA), more often affiliated to traditional rural communities, continue to reflect a similar divide. Yet both claim the same fundamental 'right' to practice hands-on clinical midwifery skills.[17] It is clear, therefore, that the lay midwife role *cannot* give us a precise match for the doula archetype, for while the contemporary doula may provide social support, she categorically *does not* provide any clinical or medical care.[18]

Many depictions of birth through the ages do nonetheless show the labouring mother, usually seated upright, with the midwife before her and additional women helpers gathered around her.[19, 20, 21, 22] It is likely that these birth supporters included a relative or trusted servant of the mother and the midwife's apprentice.[23, 24] In mediaeval Europe, a lay female figure known as the 'godsibb', an Old English term meaning 'Sister of God' or 'godparent' is documented. During the 1300s this word referred specifically to a female friend who accompanied the birthing mother, a kind of 'childbirth companion'. The 'godsibb' also helped out in a practical way, attending to general household chores, such as washing, cooking and the care of older children.[25] Although untrained in midwifery, these lay women regularly provided emotional, physical and practical support at births within their community. They may therefore have developed a keen sense of how best to support the labouring mother in an instinctive, spiritual way during her birth process. The 'childbirth servant' and the 'godsibb' may indeed have possessed many qualities of the traditional 'wise woman', albeit without the midwifery skills of the 'with woman', offering us perhaps the most likely possibility for the origins of the contemporary doula.

Modern interpretations

The contemporary term 'doula' was first coined by US medical anthropologist, Dana Raphael, in her 1973 publication *The Tender Gift: Breastfeeding.*[26] She took the word from its Greek translation meaning 'serving woman' and reinterpreted it for modern purposes as *"the person who supports the mother so that she can breastfeed."*[27] It is perhaps also interesting to note that the word 'dula' appears in South African Sesotho, meaning 'to sit.'[28] This sense may resonate for many who 'doula', for frequently time is spent *".. simply sitting or 'being' with the expectant woman or new mother, listening to her hopes and fears, .. empathising with her ups and downs."*[29] It was US childbirth and newborn experts Marshall Klaus, Phyllis Klaus, John Kennell, Penny Simkin and Annie Kennedy who, in 1992, established the current meaning of 'doula' however, to embrace the support she provides during pregnancy, labour and birth, as well as the postpartum period.[30] Research undertaken by Klaus and Kennell in the late 1970's had substantiated the value of sustained emotional and practical support for the labouring mother from another woman to increase the likelihood of physiological birth, as well as the importance of immediate contact for babies with their parents after birth to promote bonding.[31, 32] In a time of increasingly medicalised childbirth practices, absence of traditional midwifery care and subsequent lack of social support, the researchers' vision was to promote the doula as a designated female figure to 'mother the mother.'[33] In order to support the education of the doula and the development of her role, Klaus et al. duly founded the organisation *Doulas of North America (DONA),* also covering Canada and now embracing a wider international perspective. Whether she is chosen and hired independently by the parent(s), or allocated as a volunteer by the maternity care or social welfare system, *DONA*'s mission statement currently proposes *"a doula for every woman who wants one."*[34]

Although the term 'doula' initially emerged in the UK during the 1990's, the first stirrings of the doula movement did not take off until the turn of the 21st century. Set up in 1993, the *Hansy Josovic Maternity Trust* not only provided prenatal education within the Orthodox Jewish community in London, but was also probably the first organised group to offer lay companionship for birthing women in the UK. Underpinned with a strong ethos of advocacy, doulas affiliated to this group continue to work across England today.[35] A few years later, childbirth sociologist

Sheila Kitzinger, likeminded friend and colleague of *DONA*'s Penny Simkin, pioneered a campaign towards improving conditions for imprisoned mothers-to-be that led to the abolishment of the use of handcuffs during labour. Kitzinger's groundbreaking work was carried forward in collaboration with *National Childbirth Trust* (NCT) teacher, Diana Parkinson, and in 1996, the voluntary *Holloway Doula Group* (now known as *Birth Companions*) was established.[36] The aim of this group was, and still is, to provide sustained emotional and social support specifically for birthing prisoners incarcerated within London's female penal institution.

Just a year later, director of *Top Notch Nannies* agency, Jean Birtles, placed an advert in *The Guardian* inviting women who were interested in 'training to become a doula' to an open meeting, also in London. Having received an enquiry from a client for a doula and in discussion with a US doula trainer, Birtles was exploring the possibility of establishing a UK doula course. Seventeen women from around England attended the meeting, including experienced doula Liliana Lammers, who had close affiliations with primal health researcher and natural birth pioneer Michel Odent. Already known for promoting the benefits of unconditional, sustained support from an additional trusted female, Odent's reputation for protecting physiological birth was well respected within the natural birthing circles. Keen to initiate the premise of UK specific doulas, Birtles therefore enlisted Odent to deliver her doula 'training' programme and *Top Notch Nannies*' sister agency *Top Notch Doulas* (now known as *British Doulas)* was created.[37]

However, with his long term vision for UK doulas ultimately heading in a more organic, grassroots direction, it was not long before Odent parted company from Birtles and established his own doula course *Paramana*, in liaison with Lammers.[38] The desire among likeminded London women to establish a doula community was soon recognised by the then *Paramana* student, Hilary Lewin. Prompted by Lewin's enthusiasm for organising parties, a meeting was held at Odent's house on 10th February 2001, where the proposed vision for a doula organisation run by doulas for doulas was duly aired and discussed over cake. As Lewin recalls, *"It became quickly apparent that the time was right and we were about to forge something wonderful; a group of strong dedicated women is a force to be reckoned with! .. A quiet woman with a determined look in her eye voiced the ability to design a website and we were on the road, Vida (Rye) was our driving force and brought a fantastic selection of skills to the party."*[39] Thus, with the key aims of providing peer group support and promoting better accessibility to doula care for parents, *The Independent Doula Association* (later renamed *Doula UK), led by Lewin as Chair, was born.[40] It was, as Odent proclaimed, *'an historic day.'*[41]

Further to the pioneering organisations *DONA International* and *Doula UK*, the first decade of the 21st century has seen the emergence of the role of the modern doula and doula networks established across much of Europe, Australia and other continents of the world. More detailed discussion of this dissemination is presented in *Part 1. 4. The wider doula community.*

2. 21st century doulas

Essence of the doula

'essence': spirit, soul, heart, fundamental nature

> *"Doulas are just women who really, truly care about other women, on a major level."*
>
> Linda Quinn, 2010 [1]

The doula is a layperson who is experienced in birth and parenting. Usually a mother herself, she provides sustained emotional and practical support to women and couples during the childbearing year. That is not to say that a doula who has not yet had her own family or who has taken the long term decision not to have children, cannot be a sensitive and effective supporter however. She may support parents during pregnancy and birth, after the baby is born, or both, but the key lies in the *continuity* of her companionship.[2] Ideally, the doula is selected by the mother or parents-to-be as someone with whom they share a like-minded philosophy on birth and parenting, with whom they feel at ease and able to develop a trusting relationship before their baby is born. Not qualified to provide medical or clinical advice, the doula may suggest useful resources for them to access, so as to support them in making informed decisions about their journey through childbirth, in the way that feels right for them. The doula is specifically the mother's (and father's) companion, she can advocate in communications with health professionals at any time through pregnancy, labour, birth and during the postnatal period, according to their wishes.

Co-Chair of Doula UK, Bridget Baker, sees her as one who is *".. grounded, self-aware with a quiet confidence. Her instinct will not be drowned by the knowledge she needs to possess in order to work safely."*[3] A good doula will be mindful of how her own birth and parenting experiences may impact on another mother's birth or breastfeeding journey and seek the opportunity to contemplate, process and heal these within a safe environment on an ongoing basis. She will be committed to maintaining a reflective attitude to her doula work at all times, securing support from her trusted mentors as necessary. Kind, compassionate, showing respect and integrity towards both her clients and colleagues, she will not seek undue financial profit from the service she provides as a doula. With no upper or lower age restriction, the doula nonetheless needs to show fortitude in mind, body and spirit, for the sometimes long hard hours of supporting a mother through labour and birth require both physical and emotional stamina.

There are many doulas who offer additional skills in therapeutic practices such as homeopathy, aromatherapy, massage, hypnobirthing or reflexology. While these may be seen as supportive 'tools' to draw on if required, they do not necessarily make her a better doula. When a mother contacts another woman for doula support, she is looking for a fellow mother who can offer warmth and empathic support, or simply the nurturing presence of another woman - a female companion who is content to hold her hand with integrity, not necessarily someone who can offer specialist skills in non-doula related work. An exploration of the finer details of her practical role can be found in *Part 2, Guardians of Gentle Birth?*, but the fundamental essence of the doula's work is often much more about *being* than about *doing*. It can be enough for her to just sit and listen rather than constantly busy herself with offering support measures, those which may prove distracting to the labouring woman or disregarding of the emotional needs of the postnatal mother. There is no necessity or requirement for a doula to apply any therapeutic intervention other than her own calm, mindful presence.

In view of her lay status, it is not mandatory for the doula to undertake any formal training; in effect she may simply be a relative or friend of the mother-to-be who may or may not have experienced childbirth herself. The fact that she *has* completed a short course in basic preparation to work as a doula gives her access to resources she might otherwise not have known about, specific literature or online information, complementary practitioners or crisis support groups, for example. As an initial period of learning and skill development, it aims to develop her communication skills and to enhance her understanding of birth, breastfeeding and the sociological needs of the new family. Most importantly, it gives her the opportunity to begin to process her own birth experiences. It also opens the door for her to charge a fee for her services if she wishes, but it should not be confused with professional training where an extended period of study leading to qualification and statutory regulation, as in midwifery, is the outcome. While a doula course may improve the standard of her knowledge, the real essence of the doula comes from *within herself* and is not necessarily something that can be taught. Nor should it suggest the need for any certification or registration status, for these are also labels applied to trained professionals. While the doula may work in a professional way, she is not a professional worker.

Most women preparing to work as doulas do, however, choose to undertake a short programme of study before setting themselves up to offer support to the birthing family. So what might a doula need to know, and why?

Principles of doula preparation

'preparation': readiness, preparing someone or something
'training': acquiring of skills
'qualification': official requirement

"*.. the most important part of any (doula) 'training' is creating a climate for growth through self-awareness. Engendering an ability for 'stillness', reflection and life-long learning.*"

Bridget Baker, 2010[4]

We understand from research studies that having the support of a doula can improve birth and perinatal outcomes[5, 6, 7, 8] as well as the mother's overall satisfaction with her experience.[9] What has not yet been examined is exactly that which makes her support effective. Sheila Kitzinger sees the developing doula role as "*an opportunity to use skills which have not previously been recognised as marketable - understanding and insight, sympathy, warm friendship, a capacity to communicate effectively and at an intimate level.*"[10] As we have already established, these skills are not necessarily ones that can be taught and indeed, as Michel Odent remarks, "*If the focus is on the training of the doula rather than on her way of being and her personality, the doula phenomenon will be a missed opportunity.*"[11]

Some women just 'doula', often without knowing that what they do has a name, supporting expectant and new mothers and fathers is simply an integral part of their way of life. These doulas have not necessarily undertaken any course of learning, they instinctively work in response to what parents need, gleaning whatever additional information they require from books, conferences, online resources and personal communication within the birthing family's network. But there are other women who are truly drawn to doula-ing yet feel they do not have the confidence or resources they need to simply start doing it.

As a doula course leader (*Mindful Doulas*), I regularly point out to prospective students applying to my programme, the questionable issue of 'training' as a requisite. Despite suggesting that, as doulas, we are simply women supporting women, mothers supporting mothers, they mostly still feel that they would prefer to do some preparation work. I often wonder how much this stems more from a generic lack of belief in their own abilities, as women, as mothers, as birthers even, than from a genuine desire for knowledge. In addition, these women are frequently under the impression that they are not 'allowed' to work as doulas until they have undertaken a 'training' course or acquired a 'qualification'. While this is clearly not the case, in the light of such anxieties it might seem appropriate that a certain level of learning and support is provided for new doulas, over and above their personal experience. Perhaps more significantly, the new doula should have the opportunity to begin to debrief and reflect on her own birth and parenting journeys within a safe environment.

Many tears have been shed as buried emotions re-surface during our course workshops. Comments such as *"I have never told my birth story to someone who really wanted to listen before"*, *"I thought I had processed all my grief, yet there is still more in there"*, are common. Without taking the time to acknowledge, process and debrief from traumatic birth or mothering experiences in particular, new doulas may carry their unresolved issues into the birthspace or 'babymoon' of another mother or family. Not only is this inappropriate to the supportive role, the doula is also vulnerable to continuing to attract situations which mirror her own unfinished issues until she makes a commitment to addressing them within herself. Working as a doula is not about the doula, it is about the mothers, fathers and families she supports. A doula who does not take care of herself is not only unable to wholly support others, but she also runs the real risk of burning herself out.

There are a few women who may endeavour to commence doula work from a deep personal (albeit unconscious) need for emotional support themselves, and for whom it may not be immediately possible to resolve their own issues to the point at which they are ready to doula for other women. A doula course can be a way of identifying these women, and it is the course leader's responsibility not only to the student but also to the public, to support them to find the safest direction for their doula journey at this point. This might mean that the novice doula takes some time out to reflect and nurture herself, with a view to perhaps becoming emotionally strong enough to offer doula support at a later date.

The doula course can prepare the student to practice excellent listening skills, and to understand the importance of protecting the birthspace so that the labour remains undisturbed and the mother, therefore, more likely to enjoy a physiological birth.[12] It can prepare her with tools to calm and encourage a nervous father-to-be or support the mother with breastfeeding. It can guide her in knowing how to establish clear working boundaries with the birthing family as well as with any health professional she is likely to encounter. The programme can also inform her about the practicalities of setting up as a self employed person, and give her ideas on how to let her community know about who she is and what she does. Yet when she has completed her course, her learning does not stop there. As experienced doula educator Linda Quinn points out, "*A good doula is one who recognises that she will never be fully 'trained', for the day she does, is the day she needs to hang up her doula shoes.*"[13] As she sets out to start working with her first families, the novice needs mentorship from an experienced doula, someone who is her *own* doula, whether on an informal or formal basis. She needs to know that there is someone she can call on to debrief the relentless and barbaric birth she has just witnessed, or to guide her when the new mother she is working with is threatening to hit her baby over the head. Even experienced doulas need a trusted peer to turn to when a situation touches a nerve, which it will do: an unexpected miscarriage or stillbirth perhaps, or a very ill mother. Doula-ing is a way of life, and life's way is to throw curve balls from time to time.

There is no finite, standardised system for the preparation of doulas, which may be seen as a positive situation, for if the ideal is that there is a doula for everyone, so diversity in her learning and experience is surely the key. Wherever she resides, a woman coming into doula work would be well advised to choose her preparation course carefully, ensuring that the philosophy behind it resonates with the way she lives her life and that the programme leader is sympathetic to the true essence of the doula. Given her inherent nature to 'be' rather than to 'do', it could be suggested that a course based on honouring the "*celebration of childbirth*" and parenting with humility and integrity, where the student is encouraged to work in a way that mirrors ongoing reflection and commitment to service and community, would seem preferable.[14] Mindfulness of the course leader's attitude towards financial gain and approach to marketing and how this sits with the ethics of doula work, may also be advisable.

In the same way that a birth or a breastfeed cannot be rushed, neither is it compatible for the doula to push for work. Aggressive marketing and any notion that there are opportunities for financial profit to be made from doula work contradict the entire doula ethos. If the key to her role lies in her *continuity* of support and the mother's trust in her integrity, the doula will take care to ensure that she is available at all times within their agreed boundaries. For example, by booking generally no more than two births per month, she avoids the possibility of both mothers going in to labour simultaneously. If she is unexpectedly unable to be present when the mother needs her, or can only provide part-time support, the doula should offer reliable back up from a colleague. While, as doula and course leader Maddie McMahon concurs, providing 'shared' care with another local doula, whether for birth or postnatal work, can be a satisfying and successful experience for all concerned,[15] it is only acceptable when the mother (and her partner) has consented from the start, has met with both her doulas throughout and is in no doubt that the reliability of the support she is offered will not be compromised. If bringing community back to childbirth is an integral part of the essence of the doula, for her to venture outside her own community to seek work in an area that is already covered by more local doulas, on the basis of milking a potential business opportunity, may also be considered unethical. Indeed, there seems little doubt that the dynamic of doula-ing changes when a doula is chasing money. As Quinn advises her novices: *"If you don't click with the parents at that first interview, you should walk away,"*[16] for through lack of feeling some deep care towards her client, the integrity of the doula's role is surely lost.

Most women will choose to undertake an independently run, doula-led birth and/or postnatal course, usually spanning a period of days or weeks, sometimes months, marked with a final certificate of completion, such as any of those approved by *Doula UK*. A few doula organisations provide integral programmes specifically for their members: these are more likely to be midwife-led and, in some cases, offering formalised academic accreditation. Trained professionals, such as childbirth educators or complementary practitioners, may have the option to extend their skills into doula-ing under the umbrella of an affiliated professional body. All the above options are likely to include some distance learning as well as direct student-tutor interaction. Doula facilitated workshops are also available in the form of one day taster or update sessions, where women, mothers, doulas and midwives, can gather for some *"intelligent tea drinking,"*[17] unravel birth stories, explore issues such as ethics, boundaries and advocacy, and share experiences of accompanying the birthing family.

Overall, a doula preparation course is perhaps as much about the doula pursuing her own inner journey as it is about initiating her vocation as a birth or postnatal companion. It is about encouraging a reflective attitude and community spirit, a presence of mind and careful action and nurturing the confidence that it is enough just to be herself. These are qualities and, indeed, lifelong lessons for which no academic qualification or professional certification can assume to guarantee. Even if, or when, a doula chooses for any reason not to continue in her work, at the very least she can rest assured that she will have enriched her life experience through this learning. Further detailed discussion on doula education is provided in *Part 1. 3. UK 'brand' of doula* and *4. The wider doula community*.

3. UK 'brand' of doula

The lay role, why professionalise it?

'lay': without expertise/professional training in a particular field, non-professional
'professional' (v): show high degree of skill/competence, work in a 'professional' way
'professional' (n): somebody whose occupation requires extensive education or specialised training, a 'professional'

> *"There seems to be a tension around the issue of professionalisation of doulas, with some wanting to move doula practice from its origins in the lay, grass roots, community model to create another albeit non-clinical para-professional involved in childbirth."*
>
> Fiona Bogossian, 2006[1]

The UK is one of the first countries beyond North America to have wholly embraced and adapted its own 'brand' of doula on a nationwide scale. Indeed, a UK survey compiled by doula and course leader Valerie Goedkoop in 2008, highlights statistics that mirror many of the already well-established research based benefits of doula support.[2] Yet while the UK doula is to an extent modelled on that of the US, there are fundamental areas of definition where their characteristics differ, importantly around issues concerning qualification and status.

Described as 'professionally trained'[3] and 'certified', suggesting that she has acquired 'qualified' and 'expert' status, the terms used to describe the US doula present a conundrum to the UK understanding of her lay status. As DONA founder and doula educator Penny Simkin explains, this may be partly due to semantics however: in the US, the term 'professional' is more likely to mean someone who works 'in a professional way', someone who is 'reliable, honest, ethical', whereas in the UK it is more often used to describe someone who is 'a professional worker', such as a midwife or a teacher.[4] The term 'training' *is* mutually understood within both cultures to represent a 'prolonged period of study leading to professional qualification' nonetheless. The 'period of study' for US doulas may indeed lean towards a more substantial and comprehensive type of course than many of those provided within the UK, including required attendance at prenatal classes and support at births. Yet doula programmes are still categorised as 'training' - albeit for the layperson - and used to describe the period of preparation undertaken by doulas on both sides of the Atlantic. This can perhaps be misleading to the UK public, who increasingly, although not unreasonably, tend to assume that if a doula is 'trained' she must also be a 'qualified, registered professional'.

According to doula/student midwife and author of *The Father's Homebirth Handbook*, Leah Hazard - who is American born but long based in Glasgow - another critical difference between US and UK doulas is that the student doula in the US must also be assessed, for the purpose of her training, on her performance at each birth by the attending midwife. It is, Hazard suggests, as if the US doula system *"seems to seek medical approval, whereas the UK style doula works most definitely outside, or possibly parallel to, the medical system."*[5]

Education

As with any new movement, doula courses continue to emerge across the UK, ranging from the traditional, community-focused approach to the modernist, trained-professional style. The grassroots programmes are mostly run by experienced working doulas, who remain focused on the fundamental principles of the doula-ing ethos and who, even through their PR, take great care to express their connection to humanity. Cambridge based *Developing Doulas*, for example, aims to *"encourage doulas to develop a generosity of spirit that allows them to put their clients' needs above their own and a willingness to empower others at the expense of their own egos,"*[6] while *Birthing Wisdom* in Devon states that *"for many women the course is a journey of self-discovery, of delving deeply into the feminine and into 'Presence,' developing the necessary qualities to successfully support women and couples through the journey of pregnancy, birth and early parenthood."*[7] Other doula educators offer a more snapshot glimpse of the ethos behind their programmes, such as the *Holistic Birth Trust Foundation* who describe theirs as a *"learning of love"*[8] or *Conscious Birthing* who seek to provide *"non-judgmental"* doulas,[9] or *Nurturing Birth* who hail theirs the *"largest doula training organisation"* in the UK.[10]

Doula courses that are affiliated with the public services and/or are academically accredited may be at least partially led by midwives or other healthcare professionals rather than doulas however. Perhaps somewhat questionably, given the 'lay' role of the doula, for why does she need to be 'trained' by 'professionals' at all? Furthermore, by those whose line of work is substantially different from hers? Would a doctor train a midwife, or a midwife train a mental health nurse, for example? Perhaps it is the intention of such courses to 'train' what might be considered a more 'professional' kind of doula, thereby suggesting that her services are more reliable. Yet does this focus on training academic professionals not potentially create some kind of 'corporate' doula? Mental health nurse/midwife-led training organisation *Doula Consultancy Services*, who assert to be *"Innovators of doula university education"*, suggest that academic qualification is of key importance to the doula's credibility;" indeed, the *NCT*'s new birth companion course for their existing workers is also university linked.[12] Complementary therapies consultancy, *Expectancy*, presents a different perspective however, through their midwife-led Maternity Support Therapist (doula) programme for complementary therapists and Certificate in Maternity Complementary Therapies for doulas.[13] As director Denise Tiran explains, her primary concern is the issue of "*safety*" around doulas using complementary therapies. Therefore, she feels it is important that her course is formally accredited, and for any course to offer academic accreditation, Tiran adds, the trainers must be "*fully qualified academics*", midwives or otherwise.[14] Ultimately though, as *Fathers to Be* director Patrick Houser describes, if doulas are women "*who know the value and importance of bringing our children into a world filled with love, gentleness, sacredness and freedom,*"[15] their ability to support birthing families surely comes back to the essence of the doula as an individual herself, regardless of her academic status? With regard to those working *purely* in the doula role, perpetuating the notion of professionally trained, academically qualified childbirth companions can only serve to create a two-tiered level of 'lay' and 'professional' doula, as has already occurred in the US. Whether this is likely to be useful for childbearing women in the UK, who are already over-subjected to the politics of medical hierarchy, is indeed questionable.

The difficulties with attempting to professionalise the role of the doula in the UK is additionally complicated by the autonomous status of UK midwives, whose provision of emotional and spiritual support lies as much within their scope of practice as physical, clinical care.[16] Furthermore, as Australian midwife Fiona Bogossian discovered during her *Winston Churchill Travel Fellowship*, while in some cases, the US doula's role can incorporate performing clinical interventions such as vaginal examination,[17] in the UK, this procedure is strictly the midwife's remit. For a UK doula to undertake such a task would not only be seen as overstepping her boundaries, by doula organisations and statutory maternity care regulatory bodies alike, but more significantly - regardless of maternal choice or request - deemed as an intention to masquerade as a midwife and thereby be in breach of the law.[18] The rationale behind UK doula courses generally consisting only of days or weeks, rather than months or years, of preparation perhaps therefore reflects the pertinent question, what exactly is the doula being 'trained' for? Indeed, if not professionally trained, why would there be any need for her to be 'certified' or 'registered'? When under scrutiny, in the UK understanding, it would therefore appear that the doula's lay status inherently means that she is *not* professionally trained, qualified or certified/registered, for if she were, she would surely be a midwife. And in view of this, the professionalised attributes used to describe the US doula's qualification and status cannot, and *should not*, be directly transferred and applied to the UK doula.

Regulation

Given that the key to the success of her role is that she is not affiliated to the maternity care system, it seems unlikely that the professionalisation of the doula would be of any significant benefit to mothers and fathers in the UK. As Nadine Edwards, vice-chair of the Association for Improvement in Maternity Services (AIMS), points out in her discussion on the relationship between women and midwives: *"The current concept of professionalization cannot easily understand the richness of relationships and how trusting relationships contribute to safe birth."*[19] It also stirs up the thorny issue of statutory regulation, for, again, as a layperson, why might there be a need for the doula to be regulated? If a mother selects her doula because she feels an instinctive connection with her and/or because other women in her community have recommended her, the doula's regulatory status may be of little concern to her. Yet the question of potential regulation for doulas continues to raise its head, although usually when the proposer has misunderstood the inherent lay status of the doula.[20]

The standardisation of the doula's 'training' and 'practice' can only perpetuate the idea of the 'professional' worker, reducing the opportunity for diversity. Potentially it could propel her uniquely independent status into becoming just another layer within the maternity care hierarchy, stifling her freedom to work in truly individualised response to her clients, and inhibiting her ability to advocate for parents. While the essential safety of birthing families remains of paramount importance, if the idea of the doula is that she is someone with whom the parents build up a relationship of trust over time, how healthy is it to formulate this relationship from a premise of fear? If there is to be any kind of regulation of doulas at all, a system that still allows for independent choice for both doulas and parents, such as voluntary self-regulation, might seem the most appropriate option. In this case, the doula is free to choose the type of preparation that fits with her philosophy on life, birth and parenting, and which kind of doula organisation to affiliate herself with. Parents are free to select the doula that is right for them with the assurance that there is a system in place to support them should their relationship with their doula run into difficulties.

At the time of writing, the majority of UK doulas are already freely opting to be affiliated with at least one established doula network for the purpose of peer group support, further learning and reflective opportunities.

Networks

The intentions of existing UK networks appear to follow two distinct threads. The first presents as a formal core organisation or agency with established training standards, usually including some form of assessment process and status certificate. This includes independent bodies as well as government funded and charitable organisations. The second presents as a localised informal peer support group. Both types offer a form of mentorship and provide some forum for learning through sharing and reflection.

With its substantial membership listing open to all doulas working in the UK, national network *Doula UK* is the forefront example of a core organisation and leader in the field of voluntary self-regulation. When, during the first three years of its existence (2001-03), the numbers swelled rapidly from 50 to over 200 doulas, the non-profit association determined to assume responsibility for setting a 'gold standard' amongst the UK doula community, establishing some degree of a safety net for the doula hiring public. It did this by setting up a two fold criteria for membership that continues to exist today.

Firstly, all new members are required to complete a *Doula UK* 'approved' preparation course (see Resources). While *Doula UK* is not a training organisation, it has agreed what it considers to be the minimum requirements for programme content and insists that this be delivered by an experienced doula or doulas. In this way, the network assesses the quality and substance of doula courses currently on the market and approves only those that fulfil the key points detailed in its *DUK Core Curriculum*.[21] This system has been put in place by experienced doulas and doula educators, in collaboration with the *DUK Council*, which includes eminent midwives and birth activists. The second requisite is that all new members undertake the *DUK Recognition Process*. This involves an initial period of mentorship and assessment to encourage ongoing reflection on and debriefing of their work, under the guidance of an experienced doula. Having completed this process to the satisfaction of her Assessor/Mentor, the 'trainee' doula is assigned the status of *Doula UK* 'recognised' doula. It was agreed that 'recognised', to mean 'acknowledged' or 'identified', was a more appropriate term of appraisal than 'certified', to describe a layperson that has attained a certain level of skill and understanding beyond that of absolute novice. Exceptions may apply for an already experienced doula who has not completed a course approved by *Doula UK*, and who may still be accepted for membership and recognition through the Fast Track Recognition Process: her eligibility is considered by two Assessor/ Mentors on an individualised basis.

A mother or couple who enlist a *Doula UK* doula can know that she has attained a certain level of knowledge and skill as a doula, that she has agreed to work within the *DUK Philosophy*[22] and *Code of Conduct,*[23] and that she has access to an established community of experienced doulas from which to draw support and guidance on her work as necessary. As the doula does not give advice or undertake procedures, she is not responsible for the health and wellbeing of her client beyond that which is normally expected of a friend or relative. Should a parent find the need to make a complaint about a doula however, the relevant system is in place to process it within the organisation.

On a smaller scale and with a very different ethos, although with perhaps a similar view to supporting doulas and protecting the public, London doula agency *British Doulas* aims to provide the capital's public with quality assured doulas by listing on their books only those who have successfully passed through their own midwife-led 'training' and in-house vetting process. Parents are however charged a fee for the privilege of being offered a selection of potential doulas, although importantly, they are still free to interview and choose the doula that suits them best.[24]

Some schemes, such as *DUK's Hardship Fund,*[25] exist to fund doulas to undertake work for expenses only, in the case of financial difficulty on the part of the mother or couple. In Yorkshire, the *Goodwin Volunteer Doula Project* has established itself in partnership with local Primary Care Trusts (PCT), providing government funded courses and a subsequent support network for volunteer doulas. As part of the Hull based Goodwin Development Trust, a social enterprise which includes opportunities for education/training, regeneration, family support and positive health schemes within socio-economically disadvantaged areas, the *Goodwin Volunteer Doula Project* attracts women from the same local communities as the mothers they are supporting.[26] The part-time six-week 'training' programme, led by doulas, midwives and other health professionals, additionally embraces sessions on smoking cessation, domestic violence and child protection, and there are plans afoot to expand the availability of voluntary state funded doula networks in other areas of the UK.

While the intention behind the project may be ideal with regard to accessibility to doulas, particularly for more vulnerable women, a question could be raised around the doula's role as advocate. When selected and chosen by the mother, the doula's role in this aspect is clear, but what if she is answerable to the PCT because that is who has funded and facilitated her 'training'? The same might be said for doulas who are employed through the government funded *Children Centres* (formerly *Sure Start*), as it is the state which is paying their fees, although their 'training' is undertaken at their own expense. On the other hand, doulas that *do* work through the care provision or social enterprise bodies, often work with some of the most vulnerable women in the country, many of whom simply have no one else to support them (see Doula Tales).

Doulas affiliated to the charity *Birth Companions* are protecting the human rights of a similar clientele, having undertaken in-house 'training' which embraces specific skills for supporting birthing women who are in prison.[27] Of all the UK networks, it is perhaps this particular one that represents the ideal of a doula organisation: independently funded, *Birth Companions* is free of affiliations which might affect doula advocacy, yet offers free-of-charge services with doulas specifically committed to a cause. Their set-up highlights how ultimately the quality of her companionship comes down to the integrity of the individual doula, how she interprets the essence of her role and how she delivers her intention to undertake her work with the same dedication and compassion as might a family member or friend.

The first of the less formal localised peer support groups to be established was the *Scottish Doula Network*. Existing as a small network of doulas working in Scotland and cross-border with Northern England since 2001, as numbers expanded from 3 to 30, members agreed - principally to support advertising costs - to charge a nominal membership fee as from 2007. While Scottish doulas were happy to strengthen their network as a cohesive body, they remained keen to see it continue to function essentially as a peer support group. Providing an opportunity for sharing of experience and learning was, and still is, considered more important than any kind of regulatory purpose. So as to ensure that no doula in Scotland is left without access to reflective support, the *Scottish Doula Network* provides the option of informal local mentorship for those new doulas, as well as buddying for experienced doulas, who choose not to undertake the *DUK Recognition Process* or equivalent. The focus of the network is reflected in the *SDN Ethical Statement,*[28] on bringing community back to childbirth, with some doulas offering their services on an exchange basis or sliding scale fee, and with a strong connection to the ceremonial and spiritual aspects of birth and parenting. Doulas who have undertaken their preparation through the Scotland-based *Mindful Doulas* course, but who then go to work outside the UK, are also welcomed by the *SDN* as members or friends.

Whichever organisation the doula is affiliated to is likely to depend to a degree on the women and the community in which she serves, and a key issue to consider is perhaps not so much how members are prepared or 'trained', but what kind of support, ongoing learning, forum for exchange and encouragement for debriefing and reflection the organisation provides. The philosophy behind the network may also be crucial for the new doula to consider, for as previously noted, there is potentially a growing divide between grassroots doulas and those who work with a more 'corporate' approach. Yet as long as UK doulas continue to seek support from each other and to further their learning and experience, aspects which are in any case integral to their role, it seems likely that a system of voluntary self-regulation remains set to persist.

4. The wider doula community

A global movement towards protecting natural childbirth?

"She is the ultimate faith-bearer - the one who still believes even when all around have lost hope and are nay-saying - ideally she does nothing but knit nearby - but if no-one is there to protect, soothe, rub, love, smile to, cry with, pray with, hug, give strength to, believe in the mother - the doula does it ....

Nicola Goodall, 2010[1]

By 2005, a flurry of doula activity had been set off across the globe, resulting in new doula networks and the emergence of parent-led ways of approaching birth in many places beyond North America and the UK. At the time of writing, doula groups or networks are active in over half of the European countries, in Australia and South Africa; individual doulas have also appeared working in New Zealand, Latin America, the Middle East, Asia and further parts of Africa.[2, 3, 4, 5] This is in addition to the already recognised role of the lay birth supporter which exists within traditional societies in some of these countries.

So what is the reason for this action for change in attitude towards birth? Is the uptake of modern doula services merely a transient trend – the latest must-have accessory? Or rather a response to real public demand from birthing families in the light of drastic global shortages of midwives, particularly those practising individualised care and using grassroots skills?

The industrialised world

Valerie Dupin, Co-Chair of *l'association Doulas de France*, sees it as a long overdue call from childbearing women for better birth and early parenting experiences. She suggests that increased accessibility to information through the internet has meant that expectant mothers are more likely to understand their potential choices and entitlements during childbirth. Dissatisfied with the lack of appropriate and individualised care they are receiving from the medical profession, they are turning to their social network for emotional and practical support,[6] and increasingly, these parents-to-be are calling for homebirths. However, if there is no structure for midwifery services to support birth at home, as has been the case in Portugal and Spain for example, mothers and fathers have turned to lay supporters to help facilitate their wishes.[7, 8] That is not to say that doulas are attempting to substitute or replace midwives - they are not - for their agenda is to support mothers in experiencing the kind of birth that is right for them, *not* to assume responsibility for their care. Yet the authorities' fear of their insubordination is the fine line that some doulas in Europe may find themselves treading.

Indeed, local cultural and legal issues can influence the doula's position considerably, as illustrated by *l'association Doulas de France's* three year struggle to establish their right to exist (formalised in 2006). Obliged to prove to the medical profession that doulas are not underground midwives and that parents need doulas, they worked closely with *Doula UK* and Penny Simkin of *DONA,* who shared their experiences of setting up national groups in this field. To become a member of *l'association Doulas de France,* prospective doulas must undertake a two-day induction course which covers the association's *Code of Ethics* and legal issues pertaining to working as a doula in France, and also explores personal and practical boundaries for prospective doulas. Like *Doula UK, l'association Doulas de France* provides a core curriculum for education but is not a training organisation itself. Differently to their UK counterparts, France's trainee members do not commence whichever doula programme they have chosen to undertake until *after* joining the association, a course of preparation that includes an apprenticeship period of supporting three birthing families throughout their birth and early parenting experience. However, French doulas are restricted by law to supporting women and couples only with a midwife present, for fear that they may otherwise be practising underground midwifery. Neither are they permitted to act as advocate for the mother, for fear of the midwife being contradicted; only the father or other birth partner can legally adopt this role.[9, 10] Nonetheless, principal voices in the doula and natural childbirth arena have been presenting at *l'association Doulas de France's* annual conference since 2003, which aims to raise public awareness and understanding of the doula role across Europe.

Equally significantly, in the Netherlands where midwives are traditionally reputed for providing homebirth support and women centred care, many mothers feel that midwifery services have become eroded and birth, as a result, more medicalised.[11] In addition, the amount of state provided labour and postnatal support from maternity nurses (*kraamverzorgenden*), has also been cut.[12] However, in a culture where the importance of emotional and practical support around the time of childbirth is already well established, Dutch doulas appear to have emerged relatively organically. According to Canadian-born, Amsterdam-based doula, Jennifer Walker, it was expectant mother Saskia Bruyn who raised the profile of the doula when she unsuccessfully sought one for the birth of her baby in 2001. Bruyn later co-wrote the booklet *'De Doula - emotionele ondersteuning bij de bevalling'*

(2006) with Thea van Tuyl,[13] a childbirth educator who established one of the two original Dutch doula training programmes alongside colleagues Dora Kroon and Trudie Kamphuis in 2006. Debra Pascali-Bonaro of *DONA International* led the other course, in conjunction with one of Holland's first doulas Esther Kokkelmans. As in the UK, there is no statutory requirement to join *The Dutch Professional Association for Doulas*, although differently from *Doula UK*, membership is open to both those who have undertaken a programme of training as well as doulas who have learned through experience only.[14]

At the other end of the spectrum, in Portugal, childbirth is highly medicalised and the role of the midwife has long been replaced by that of the obstetric nurse. Homebirth is rare and the level of fear in the hospital birthing room significant, with informed emotional support for the labouring woman notoriously lacking.[15] According to Portuguese doula, Catarina Castro, few WHO recommendations for childbirth are upheld by Portugal's obstetric system. In 2005 therefore, she explains, a small group of women attended Odent's *Paramana* doula course and then started up their own training programme, which led to the foundation of the *Association Doulas de Portugal*. Two further associations for the 'humanization of birth' in Portugal enlist doula courses from abroad, including *DONA International*. The role of the doula in Portugal has met with much resistance from the medical profession, although Castro feels this is slowly changing, with couples being better informed about gentle birth. A handful of doctors are now embracing the idea of natural birth and a few homebirth midwives have an active presence.[16] The main hurdle for the Portuguese doulas seems to be in establishing harmonious and proactive relationships with the existing maternity system and ousting their initial reputation for being a challenge to authority.

Courses such as those run by *Paramana* and *DONA International* have done much to shape the preparation of doulas in other European countries too. Belgium's *Doulas de Belgique*, Hungary's *Association of Hungarian Doulas* and Spain's *doulasbarcelona* have incorporated Odent's principles into their own locally devised programmes.[17, 18] In Germany, doula educator and author, Melanie Schöne runs her *DONA* initiated course comprising of three weekends over a period of 9 months. This leads to certification once students have supported at three births, completed their required reading and attended a preparation for birth class speaking about the role of the doula. The number of German doulas has risen dramatically since 2007, Shöne adds, and two organisations, *Doulas in Deutschland e.v.,* for which doula Kristina Wierzba-Bloedorn produces a monthly newsletter, and *Gesellschaft fur Geburtsvorbereitung*, have been established.[19, 20] On a smaller scale, some doulas working in Ireland and Norway, for example, are UK 'trained' through *Mindful Doulas* and *Developing Doulas,* while *Nurturing Birth* has prepared doulas in Switzerland and Finland, among others. Distance-learning organisation *Childbirth International* has doula members in European countries including Cyprus, Greece, Serbia and Turkey.[21, 22, 23, 24]

Perhaps the oldest existing doula network in mainland Europe however, is Sweden-based ODIS (Organisation for doulas and childbirth educators in Scandinavia), which was established in 1999.[25] Indeed, of the recent available evidence, two key papers on doulas have been written by Swedish researchers. Both studies support the idea that mothers are more likely to feel satisfied with their birth experience when having been accompanied by a doula.[26] Lundgren (2010) additionally states that the roles of the midwife and doula need to be viewed differently, given that many midwives are no longer able to provide continuous support and suggests that any provision of social support now lies essentially with the doula.[27]

Meanwhile, efforts to develop a European Doula Network remain ongoing. Building on the European Doulas Guide, published by *l'association Doulas de France* in 2007 as a focus for communication, sharing and support,[28] a group of German-speaking doula trainers presented a position report in Switzerland in 2009. It outlined minimal standards for the training and role of a doula working in any European country, plus the aims of and criteria for membership of the proposed network.[29] By 2010, however, they realised that setting common standards for doulas across Europe was no longer a priority, as the individual national associations were already effectively achieving this. Rather, the steering group's most recent document proposes *"an open European network for all doula associations willing to develop and grow in quality"* and includes a Europe-relevant definition of the fundamental role and (common) responsibilities of a doula.[30]

The inspiration initiated by *Doula UK* can be found amongst doula communities on other continents too. Founder member, Vida Rye of *NurtureNZ*, has been keeping the doula concept alive in her adopted home country of New Zealand since 2002,[31] while former early member, Lisa Chalmers, established Perth based *Australian Doulas* in 2007. Although further doula networks are in existence around Australia (see Resources), Chalmers' organisation uniquely provides volunteer doulas for a local refugee project and doula courses for established refugees; with recent government funding, *Australian Doulas* are set to expand into the rural areas and within Aboriginal communities.[32] In addition, several DUK approved courses have trained doulas now working in the United Arab Emirates (*Nurturing Birth*),[33] Kenya, Zimbabwe and Japan (*Mindful Doulas*),[34] even Barbados (*Developing Doulas*).[35]

Unlinked to the UK, although well established nonetheless, Johannesburg based doula Maria Sterrenberg has been working as a birth companion in South Africa since 2001. Drawing on local traditional community roots in social support during childbirth, she founded *The Village Doula Training* in 2004.[36] Her year-long course, delivered in collaboration with doula colleague, Rosalia Pihlajasaari, comprises of six weekly workshops, covering aspects including 'Neutrality & Clearing' and 'Doula "Work" - Sitting & Sitting', followed by a period of mentored practical experience.[37] National umbrella organisation *Doulas of South Africa*, chaired by Pihlajasaari, was set up in 2009 with the aim of providing *"..awareness and support to doulas, the public and related health care providers through: regulation.. (and) education..;"*[38] 'regulation' being that of a voluntary or non-statutory nature, as previously discussed in *Part 1. 3. UK 'brand' of doula.*

Strictly an online/distance learning course, independent organisation *Childbirth International* has nonetheless facilitated doula education in far flung parts of the world - from Peru to the Philippines, from Israel to India, from Chile to China – locations where women might not otherwise have had access to a formalised programme.[39]

The developing world

The medicalisation of childbirth may have been established as the norm across the industrialised world, in the name of preserving lives and maintaining safety during childbirth, yet the caesarean birth rate in US and UK, for example, remains much higher [24.6% in England (2007-08), 24.7% in Scotland (2008), 31.8% in US (2007)][40, 41, 42] than the figure of 10-15% perceived as 'necessary' by the World Health Organisation.[43] Increasingly, women in developing countries are aspiring to medically managed birth too, resulting in even higher caesarean statistics: 39% in Mexico (2000), for example, and 34% in Thailand (2005).[44, 45] Modern medicine may indeed save lives in the case of emergency or medical complication, yet when a woman in a developing country with a straightforward pregnancy gives birth in a city hospital far from her local community, she is at risk of missing out on much of her core body of essential social support. The reality for this mother may be that she has limited access to fulfilling her basic human needs, such as nutrition and hydration, while she is in hospital, a factor that becomes increasingly significant when she has experienced surgical delivery. Although one Brazilian study shows how some women perceive that a medicalised birth means they will receive a better quality of maternity care,[46] the previously noted figures do little to suggest that this approach is supportive of the physiological birth process. In fact, it could be suggested that medicalisation has usurped/is usurping the role of social support during the time around childbirth, when perhaps all that is needed for women to feel safe and confident enough to give birth naturally, is to know that familiar trusted women, their mothers, sisters and grandmothers, are nearby.

Conclusion

It seems that the rise in the presence of the modern doula may therefore be due to a global need amongst women who have long been subjected to interventional obstetric practice and the erosion of appropriate midwifery services, to return faith, trust and community to birth. The doula fits the missing link, the key to redressing the balance; for as women's awareness is raised of how and why gentle birth is important for the long-term health and wellbeing of families, so they seek a way of achieving this. In the doula, new mothers can find both female confidante, who does not fear the powers of birth, and fellow mother or sister figure, helping her to feel safe and nurtured along the way.

There nonetheless remains an ongoing call for more midwives to redress the balance between medical management and the safe unfolding of birth physiology, although the reality of this may be folly. As much due to the lack of available funding, the need for a radical rethink on the way midwives are trained and supported, to incorporate the fundamental skills of both 'wise woman' and 'with woman', is also a key issue.

The engagement of an independent doula may, in some countries, mean shifting the financial burden from the state to the individual, yet even in the case of state funded doula services, these will cost considerably less than their midwifery equivalent. Perhaps more significantly, the presence of the doula shifts both the responsibility and power for protecting natural, gentle birth from the care provider to the service user, a notion that could potentially revolutionise the way birth is regarded and experienced, not only by childbearing women but also by those who attend them.

Part Two - GUARDIANS OF GENTLE BIRTH?

1. Birth space, Safe place: role of the birth doula

"Open heart, strong hands. Be present, listen, feel her, trust your instincts. And remember - I have birthed my children ... she will birth this child her way, with her power, be with her and let her feel your faith in her."

Jennifer Walker, 2010[1]

That the support of an additional person during labour and birth, who is not part of the hospital system, can make a difference to the positive outcome for both mother and baby is clear from an array of studies.[2] Evidence shows that there is less uptake of opiate pain medication including epidurals or requirement for augmentation of labour,[3, 4] and increased maternal satisfaction with the birth experience.[5, 6] The presence of the doula is also known to support the father to enjoy and participate in the birth of his baby at his own level of comfort.[7, 8] Perhaps the most striking of these statistics, in today's climate of soaring caesarean section rates, is that such sustained one-to-one support during labour can reduce the chances of the mother experiencing a caesarean birth by up to 50%.[9, 10] So what is it about the role of the doula that enhances the birth journey for parents?

The relationship between a birth doula and mother or parents-to-be can begin at any time during pregnancy, although ideally before around 32 weeks, so as to allow plenty of time to nurture a mutual understanding and prepare together for the birth itself. Sometimes there may be a situation where the doula is called on at the last minute, for example, if a couple have unexpectedly separated and the mother has no other support; in this case, the doula's utmost discretion and integrity is called for, to do the best she can for the mother within a limited timescale. Usually however, the doula meets with the expectant mother or parents initially on a no-obligation basis, to explore if they are well suited to one another. She will listen to their expectations of her support during labour and then specifically clarify the services that she is able to offer. At this point, she will also reiterate that her role is not intended as a replacement for the midwife. She will usually leave a contract with the mother (or couple) to sign and return to her with their deposit should she decide to book her. If her fee presents potential financial hardship for her client, the doula may be able to offer a sliding scale fee or apply to a local doula organisation, such as the *Doula UK Hardship Fund* (if she is a member), for her expenses, meaning that the mother pays a small nominal fee only. It is the parents' prerogative, and preferable for the doula who is chosen, that they interview a number of doulas (where available) before deciding with whom they feel most comfortable.

Once engaged, the doula will plan to have at least two substantial face-to-face sessions with the mother and father, to go over any previous birth experiences and to prepare for the upcoming labour. Many women turn to doulas following a traumatic first birth, often a caesarean, in the hope that they will have a gentle physiological birth second time round. The doula will listen to the previous birth story from both the mother and father's perspectives and explore with them how they might work towards protecting a natural process this time. In the case where it was a caesarean or forceps birth, considering at what point in the labour the process slowed down or became complicated, inviting medical intervention, and the possible reasons as understood by the parents for this, can help pave the way for avoiding a repeat story. It may be that there were clear medical indications for clinical assistance, on the other hand it is possible that the labour was 'disturbed' in a more subtle way, for example, by strangers entering the room, questions directed at the mother or drugs administered to her for pain management. Any of these disturbances can occur - especially within the busy hospital environment - where the birthspace is not effectively protected and may affect the flow of hormones such as oxytocin, which keeps the mother's womb contracting, or endorphins which are the body's natural pain killers, slowing down or even arresting the birth process. The doula may be the first person to raise and discuss this fundamental, yet well documented information with the parents.[11, 12] Yet the doula will never offer or provide advice, rather she will guide the mother to address any specific questions she may have about her, or her baby's, health and wellbeing during the current pregnancy to the midwife. What the doula *can* do, is to signpost the parents towards further resources where they will be able to find information to help them in their decision making process, to support them to set up the birth environment and care that is right for them.

The mother is invited to keep in touch with her birth doula by phone or email as and when she needs during the rest of her pregnancy. Sometimes the doula may be invited to accompany the mother, alongside or instead of her partner, to her prenatal visits with the midwife or obstetrician. From 38 weeks through the pregnancy, the doula will go 'on call' for the mother until the baby comes, so that she is immediately contactable 24 hours a day. Once labour starts, the doula is available as soon as the mother needs her; this may be by telephone at first until labour becomes more established. Then the doula will come to the mother's home to support her and her partner until she is ready to go into hospital to give birth, or to call the midwife for her homebirth.

A feeling of safety and privacy is paramount to the way a woman will labour. If she is interrupted by stress or fear, her body will produce the hormone adrenalin, which acts to override oxytocin, the essential labour hormone. Having the company of another woman alongside, one who has usually experienced childbirth and who she knows and trusts to 'be there' for her, the labouring mother is more likely to feel safe and protected. Hence the idea that the doula 'mothers the mother.'[13] Although this has formerly been seen as part of the modern midwife's role, with many state funded resources - such as the UK's NHS - stretched to their limits, the hospital midwife may be looking after more than one labouring women at a time, or the homebirth midwife may arrive only to attend the actual birth, providing little more than essential clinical care.

When the father-to-be witnesses his partner in physical pain and/or emotionally overwhelmed, he may experience feelings of frustration, disempowerment, even anger, generating a surge of adrenalin in his body.[14] This can feed into the fears of the mother and heighten the stress in the room. But when he sees the doula - with whom he already has an established relationship - sitting quietly and calmly nearby, unperturbed by what she knows is normal behaviour for a woman in labour, he is more likely to understand that there is no cause for concern. The father is also comfortably able to leave the room for some time out if he needs to, especially if the midwife is not present at the time, without feeling guilty that he is leaving his partner alone without a known and trusted companion.

The doula may assist the mother with position changes according to her wishes, always being led by the mother so as to encourage instinctive behaviour. She may apply some light massage or complementary techniques, such as aromatherapy, homeopathy or reflexology, that she is additionally trained in. She may dance with the mother, she may use non-interventional techniques to encourage the baby's passage through the pelvis, such as Ina May Gaskin's 'shaking the apple tree' or sacral pressure or rocking using a 'rebozo' (traditional multipurpose length of cloth used in Mexico).[15, 16] The parents may ask her to sit outside the birthing room and literally 'guard' the door, so that they can enjoy some privacy together, because that is what feels right for them. Or she may curl up in a corner, close her eyes and quietly 'be' until the baby is ready to come. According to Liliana Lammers, an 'authentic' doula will often do very little in the birthspace, she may even enter a meditative state or light sleep. Yet she is always *listening* to the mother, not only with her ears, but also with her whole body, and when she 'feels' the baby coming down into the birth canal, she becomes wholly present again in readiness to support the mother's needs during the birth.[17] This sense of 'feeling' the mother's birth process in their own bodies is a phenomenon which I have experienced and which has also been expressed to me by a number of other doulas and birth supporters.

In the UK, every woman is entitled to have a midwife attending her for the birth of her baby, and only a midwife (or medical doctor) is permitted by law to "*assume responsibility*" for her "*medical or midwifery care*"[18] during this time. However, some mothers and couples are choosing to birth without an attending midwife (freebirth), which they are entitled to do if they so wish. While it is against the law for any person, lay or professional, to pose as a registered midwife or doctor, it is not against the law for a doula to provide emotional and practical support for a labouring woman in the same way as any female friend or relative might do, even in the absence of a midwife.[19] But should a doula find herself supporting a mother who has planned to freebirth (sometimes called 'unassisted birth') she needs to be very clear about her boundaries as a layperson. At no time should she be touching or catching a baby emerging from the mother's womb, for this could be seen as acting as the midwife, and is categorically outside her working boundaries. If a midwife is not present to assist in this process as needed, for whatever reason, *the mother or her partner* can gently guide and catch their baby themselves. In the case where the unassisted birth is unplanned because the midwife has not arrived in time, the partner may wish to receive guidance on how to support the baby's birth from a hospital midwife over the phone. The doula can help by gathering pillows or cushions to lay around or under the mother for when the baby emerges, and by preparing a warm towel or blanket to wrap around the pair once the mother has gathered her baby close, next to her skin. The midwife will attend to the baby's cord when she arrives, but in the case of a planned freebirth, cord care becomes the responsibility of the mother or her partner. It may be that they have chosen to have a Lotus Birth (see Resources), where the cord is never severed and the placenta remains attached to the baby until it separates at the baby's umbilicus in its own time.

In the excitement of the moments following birth, when all eyes tend to be on the baby, the doula takes care to stay focused on the mother. Until the placenta is delivered, the birth is not (clinically) complete and the midwife cannot leave the room. Depending on whether the mother has chosen the actively managed third stage - with oxytocic drugs, cord cutting and the midwife's assistance to deliver the placenta - or to allow the process to unfold physiologically in its own time, at least part of the first hour after birth will be spent waiting for the placenta to come. Either way, evidence has shown that encouraging the mother to enjoy skin-to-skin contact with her baby is important[20, 21] and this may or may not be well supported by the midwife. The nuzzling or suckling of the baby at the mother's breast helps to encourage her body to keep producing oxytocin, to keep her womb contracting in order to expel the placenta. The doula's role is to be mindful of maintaining a calm, quiet, warm environment, of perpetuating the hopefully positive atmosphere of the birth, so that the mother's hormones remain undisturbed and she is able to let go of her placenta with ease. If the midwife has left following the delivery of the placenta, the doula may continue to provide emotional support for the mother as she offers her baby the breast. Once the third stage is complete however, a prudent doula will sense the right moment to withdraw to leave the new family to enjoy some private time together.

That the parents have considered and prepared well for a birth environment in which they feel safe, with support people they trust, can go a long way towards protecting gentle, or at least positive birth. And so much the better if the attending midwife, practising mother-led care, has been able to be present throughout the birth journey too. Sometimes however, despite everyone's best efforts, the baby will have his own agenda and need some help to be born safely. What then is the doula's role if labour and birth do not go as the parents had hoped?

As we have already established, the key to the success of doula support is her continuity of presence. She does not change shift, she is constantly at the side of the parents-to-be until the baby is born – however long that may take. This does not change when the birth process becomes complicated. Sometimes the mother or father may not fully understand a procedure that the midwife or doctor has just suggested, why it is required or how it works. Sometimes, the mother may not want to go ahead with a procedure but is too afraid to ask for further clarification or to say no. In this situation, while the work the doula has done with the couple prenatally may have given the mother's partner the confidence to advocate, it is possible for the doula to act on behalf of the mother, although *only* at her behest, to request a recap from the trained staff or further exploration into the options.

Where an emergency situation arises, when the mother or baby may need immediate medical attention and are rushed into the operating theatre without time to prepare the birth partner or even take him along too, he can be left bereft, terrified and without any real understanding of what is happening or why. It is usual that only one support person is able to accompany the mother into theatre in any situation, and this will usually be the birth partner unless the doula is the only support person, in which case she may be able to go in too. But in the case where both birth partner and doula are waiting in the birthing room for the mother to come out of theatre, the doula can be of real support to the father. Even when a mother has chosen to give birth by planned caesarean, for whatever reason, the doula has a place in providing emotional and practical support to both parents. After all, as experienced doula Daz Mickwitz reiterates, *"It's her birth. It's not about what the doula wants."*[22] Ultimately, when the mother and father feel they have led their maternity care, been listened to and had their wishes and thoughts respected along the way, even if a caesarean or other instrumental birth becomes necessary, this can still be a positive experience.

The birth doula usually concludes her supportive role through the birth journey with at least one postnatal visit to the mother and her new family. This provides everyone who was present at the birth the opportunity to 'sit and drink tea' and go over what happened, to marvel, to commiserate, to explore, to rejoice. Regardless of whether the birth has gone well or not, mothers need to talk about their experience, fathers and sometimes babies too, to unravel what has been an extraordinary life event for them. Listening to the birth story is an important part of the doula's role. Some birth doulas will mark the moment with photos or a diary of the mother's birth journey, others may simply leave a card of congratulations. Unless she is continuing to work for the family as a postnatal doula, it may be the last time she spends time with them in her doula role and it can be useful to bring closure to their relationship as such, so that the boundaries between them are left clear.

At the time of writing, a birth doula's charges for (at least) two prenatal sessions, up to 4 weeks on call, support throughout labour and birth, and one (sometimes two) postnatal visits, including unlimited phone or email contact throughout the period of support, are likely to be around £500-£800 (approximately €750). Costs can vary considerably however, depending on the doula's experience, whether she offers a sliding scale or whether the mother requires additional prenatal meetings. Anyone seeking to hire an independent doula is encouraged to contact the individuals directly to discuss their terms or, alternatively, to contact their local voluntary doula initiative where the service is free or on an expenses-only basis.

2. Continuum parenting: role of the postnatal doula

".. research reveals a great deal about the experience of babies living with mothers who feel depressed or angry, almost always because they are insufficiently supported."

Sue Gerhardt, 2004, p.57[1]

The research in support of the role of the postnatal doula may not be as extensive as that of the birth doula, but importantly we do know that new mothers are more likely to establish and continue breastfeeding when they have a known, trusted companion available to them during the postnatal period.[2,3,4] Equally significantly, evidence suggests that the maternal-infant bonding process is enhanced and the risk of postnatal illness is less likely amongst mothers supported by doulas.[5,6] *"We don't have postnatal depression in my country"* a Malaysian student once pointed out to me. She suggested that this was because it was traditional for the new mother's female family members to gather round her, 'godsibb' style, to cook and keep house, to care for other children during the time following birth, so that she is able to enjoy a 'lying in' period with her new baby to recover physically and to support her emotional wellbeing.

It is perhaps also useful to look at the bigger picture, to consider that when a mother has experienced the gentle birth of her baby in a protected and well supported environment, she is more likely to be able to engage and bond with her baby without the hindrance of a painful caesarean wound for example, or frightening memories caused by post traumatic stress. Psychotherapist and author, Sue Gerhardt, states that the key time in the development of a baby's brain is during the first three months of life; a baby whose mother is emotionally unwell and struggling to share her love with him during this period, may suffer the impact for rest of his life.[7] So the benefits not only from being breastfed, which are well established, but also from having an emotionally healthy mother cannot be underestimated in view of the long-term health and wellbeing of the baby.

The postnatal period is an extraordinary time, whether for the first or subsequent occasion of becoming a new mother. The physical impact of what equates to having run a marathon while giving birth is one thing, but in tandem with the emotional rollercoaster of changing hormones, hopes and fears and extra demands made on the mother, makes for a huge transition. The mother needs time with her new baby, just 'hanging out' time, for them to get to know each other, for her to recover her physical strength, for the baby to land and find his place within his new family. The social expectation that everything will 'get back to normal' at some point after having a baby, although whether within a week, a month or a year, varies widely. Yet nothing *is* ever the same again, nothing will ever be as it was before she had her baby, and being reassured that things can still be alright, even great - if different - despite this, may go a long way towards supporting a healthy transition into her new role. What better than having her own mother or sister, who has already had or started her own family, to accompany her on this journey? To show her through their own acts of mothering, how to be?

This may be fine for the new mother who has enjoyed a positive experience of having been mothered or parented herself, and who holds a currently respectful, loving relationship with her family members. But what of women whose experience of these interactions has been dysfunctional or abusive? And what of those who live geographically too far from their family for their continued presence to be feasible? It is possible that a friend or neighbour could be available to take the place of relatives in providing social support, but alternatively there is the option of enlisting a postnatal doula.

The postnatal doula ideally meets with the mother or parents before their baby is born, again on a no-obligation basis, to discuss the expectations and boundaries of her role as well as her potential hours of work. She may take one week's wages in advance as a non-refundable deposit on booking, when contracts are exchanged. She often starts work at around a week to a fortnight after the birth, usually around the time that the mother's partner is returning to work. Many parents, however, enlist doula support from soon after the birth, especially if they feel nervous or inexperienced in the care of a newborn.

The doula works flexibly to fit in with her client's needs and depending on what kind of birth the mother experienced and what other family commitments the mother is responsible for, the doula may come in three days, five mornings or two afternoons a week, even for the odd sleepover. Yet while she is usually open to doing whatever needs to be done to support the mother's time with her new baby, the doula is not a cleaner or a home help and neither is she a nanny or a maternity nurse. She may prepare an occasional meal or run the hoover over the carpet from time to time, collect older children from school, hang out a load of washing or pick up a few groceries when the mother is not able to do so, but the idea is that she facilitates the new mother to gain confidence and competence in her role, rather than doing it for her.

This is a skill in itself and caring attention paid to individualised need can be key to the success of this. The postnatal doula is sensitive to the style of parenting her clients have chosen, whether continuum style where the mother 'wears' her baby, carrying him in a sling all day and co-sleeping at night,[8] or routine style where the baby is kept to strict schedules around feeding, sleeping, fresh air, activities etc.[9] While she does not necessarily clean toilets, the doula may be happy to sit with the baby whose mother needs to go for a run every day, because this is what she knows will help her to prevent postnatal depression recurring for example, or walk the dog on a freezing windy day for the mother whose baby who is suffering cold symptoms and who would prefer to keep him indoors. Where there are twin babies or toddler siblings, the doula can provide a welcome extra pair of hands, simply in getting through the day. Conversely, some postnatal doulas berate the fact that they have done little more than make a cup of tea and a sandwich for their client and kept her company all morning while she has rested and breastfed her baby. Yet having someone who is open and listening in a non-judgmental way to her story, or who is simply a companionable contact with the outside world, can be an empowering and healing experience for the new mother.[10] The postnatal doula can also provide a sounding board for parents, as they explore their parenting options and work through the many small, and not so small, decisions that need to be made during the early weeks after birth.

It is not a requirement for the postnatal doula to be additionally trained as a breastfeeding counsellor, yet since much of her time is likely to be absorbed in encouraging the breastfeeding mother, undertaking some study around the lay person's role in breastfeeding support can be useful. A positive experience of having breastfed her own babies may mean that she brings a positive attitude, although as with birth, no two mothers or babies are ever the same and the doula will be mindful to guard against expecting too much of a mother who is struggling. Knowing when and where to signpost by keeping a list of local trained breastfeeding counsellors, breastfeeding drop-in clinics or at least access to a helpline for mothers to contact directly, is paramount.

When things are not going so well, particularly with regard to the new mother's emotional health, the doula may be the first person to become aware of this. It may be down to her to gather the partner or significant others together, with the mother, to encourage them to work out how they can best support her to go forward from this point in the way that is right for her. Whether she would like to consult her GP or Health Visitor, or an independent counsellor or support network in order to gain some specialist support for example. Postnatal illness can be frightening and distressing for the mother as well as those around her, sometimes the only person she is able to relate to is another mother who has experienced the same thing.[11] The doula is likely to know of local resources where her client can access this kind of support.

Likewise, when things are going well and the mother is flourishing in her new role and her baby is thriving, the doula can begin to point her in the direction of further support networks appropriate to the next stage of her parenting journey. By the time the usual 6-8 week endpoint for the postnatal doula's role is in sight, her client may already have joined a local mother and baby group, and is perhaps planning to attend postnatal yoga classes or baby massage sessions. The doula may plan to mark her final visit by inviting the mother and baby out for a walk and a coffee or to the cinema perhaps, thereby honouring their time together yet keeping the boundaries clear into the future.

At the time of writing, independent postnatal doula charges fall between £10-25 (approximately €18) per hour, usually payable on a weekly basis, although again it is worth contacting local doulas directly as fees can vary. Some doulas work voluntarily, for expenses only or on an exchange or sliding scale basis, so in principle, there is a doula for every woman.

3. Doulaing: social support or return to traditional midwifery?

"Too many Midwives have identified with the oppressor, learned to speak the conquerer's language, and otherwise been vanquished to emerge as obstetrically-trained 'Medwives.'
Jeannine Parvati Baker, 2005[1]

In many ways, to address this question brings us back full circle to where we started at the beginning of this book, and is perhaps all the more pertinent in the light of rumblings of a traditional midwifery movement afoot in Europe at the time of writing.[2] I would first like to pay tribute to all the many midwives across the world who continue to provide outstanding care - often way beyond the call of duty - to the mothers and families they work with. For without these role models, there would be no precedent for the ideal support for birthing families that I refer to throughout this text. And I say midwives, rather than doulas, because if every midwife was able to work in the way that midwifery was originally intended, the modern doula's role might be very different – with an increased focus on practical and physical measures perhaps, and much less requirement for advocacy and counselling.

Despite these midwives' best efforts however, there is no doubt that there are some women who are still not receiving the care and support that they need, or are entitled to, from their midwife, whether during pregnancy, labour or the postnatal period.[3] Evidence does not yet determine the reasons for this, although poor morale and lack of resources in the workplace may be contributing factors. Vice-chair of the Association for Improvement in Maternity Services (AIMS), Nadine Edwards, midwifery researcher Jo Murphy-Lawless and midwifery tutor, Professor Rosemary Mander suggest, perhaps more pertinently, that until the *way* midwives are trained and further supported in their practice is re-examined and overhauled, no real change in attitude and approach is likely to come about.[4] It is also clear that a climate of bullying persists within midwifery culture, often aimed at the very midwives who are respectful and supportive of how a mother wishes her labour to unfold - even if that excludes routine procedures - and who are doing their best to protect the mother's birth space and 'babymoon' at all costs.[5] Notoriously, although not exclusively, midwifery care is most quantifiably successful - low caesarean birth rates, high satisfaction with the birth experience, high breastfeeding rates - when implemented by those employed within small midwife-led birthing centres or where the community midwifery service is strong, as well as by those working independently of any state-provided system. Given all the reasons previously discussed around the mother's need for privacy, respect and a feeling of safety with like-minded supporters, this makes sense and is reflected in the remarkable statistics of Scotland's NHS Montrose Maternity Unit or London's Albany Midwifery Practice, for example.[6, 7] Yet, despite the fact that physiological birth is cheaper for service providers and therefore more cost effective for governments, it is these 'guardians of normal birth' who are regularly subjected to witch-hunts from the medical authorities. The Albany's 12 year contract with King's College Hospital was terminated in November 2009 pending allegations of unsafe practice; allegations that at the time of writing in July 2010 have still to be substantiated.[8] Also in the UK, the professional status of independent midwives remains at ongoing risk due to lack of availability of indemnity insurance.[9] In Germany, a recent change in policy now requires that homebirth midwives do vaginal examinations whether or not they feel this is clinically necessary and regardless of the mother's wishes.[10] Hungarian obstetrician and experienced homebirth midwife, Agnes Gereb, faces a prison sentence for supporting women to birth at home, a option considered unsafe and unsuitable by the medical profession in Hungary.[11] The tragedy of these stories lies in the double-edged sword of what mothers know they need for themselves and what the systems that govern midwifery care decide that mothers need. The bottom line is that, for any change to be formally endorsed, the call principally needs to come from women themselves. One of the reasons why a mother may hire a doula is to secure appropriate support for herself during labour if she lives in an area where midwives are in short supply, especially at a homebirth. However, when the midwife fails to attend in time due to staffing constraints, the doula can find herself in the position of being asked by parents to call the paramedics (who are not trained in midwifery or obstetrics) or literally to 'catch' the baby herself, thereby agitating a normal physiological event into an unnecessary drama, even perceived as an 'emergency.'[12, 13] Furthermore, as we have previously learned, where mothers are struggling to find midwives who are able and willing – sometimes at the midwife's peril - to be on their side, they are choosing to freebirth instead.[14]

But what of midwives that become doulas and doulas that become midwives, as a way of instigating change? In many ways, the doula role is potentially halfway to midwifery. In her long experience of sitting with labouring women, watching her body language, listening to her voice as labour progresses and the baby is born, or being with new mothers, hearing the way she expresses herself as she passes through the ups and downs of her new role, the doula is bound to accumulate some grassroots midwifery skills, even without realising it. What better grounding to carry through into formal midwifery training? Likewise, the midwife who has left the profession due to the restrictions the system places on her abilities to be both 'with- and wise-woman', is surely in a potentially ideal position to continue offering mother-led support to birthing women and their families by working as a doula. Yet through undertaking the style of midwifery training as it currently stands, the doula may find her fundamental with-woman skills eroded, as she is expected to care for women predominately with epidural anaesthesia in situ, for example, or spend only moments with the postnatal mother due to time constraints. The estranged midwife may find it necessary to spend a period of time de-midwife-ing herself, time to shed the prevailing sense of watching her back, to let go of 'giving advice' and begin adopting a non-directive approach in order to feel wholly able to trust the mother's process again.

Perhaps, however, it is this very conundrum that presents an opportunity to propose the development of a new type of midwifery training programme; one orientated towards traditional midwifery practice, one that instils confidence in midwives to listen and wait, a formalised lay midwifery option? It could be that midwives who pass through such a training will inherently cultivate a supportive environment for the students following behind, thereby inspiring a more cohesive, respectful and creative system within which to work, the very dynamic of which is likely to rub off positively on mothers too. The system adopted in the US is potentially a useful model, where the hospital midwives are obstetric nurses and those that attend homebirths or work in community birthing centres are lay midwives, both types are trained and accredited to the same standard, albeit through different approaches.

Indeed, it is vital that women have access to midwives, yet when no midwife is perceived as better than the midwife on offer, surely something is drastically wrong? Even where arguably excellent midwifery practice has been implemented, directive support that disturbs the mother's instincts and potentially precipitates a problematic birth can leave her still wanting, as American birth activist and writer Rachel Kellum respectfully illustrates. With her firstborn daughter Sage, Rachel experienced a traumatic managed birth in hospital; she then birthed her son Grey (despite shoulder dystocia) in the open air by their mountain cabin attended by midwives. The following extract is taken from her third baby's story, *The Birth Rite of Samuel Rune,* where Rachel chose to freebirth with her partner Geo, in their basement flat.

"The moment of the shoulders is the moment the midwives, in their loving caution, took from me at Grey's birth. I don't regret a minute of Grey's birth, or the assistance of these women. They were my healers. I needed them at that point in my life as a wounded mother. I had been lied to at Sage's birth, and they told me the truth. I had been afraid, and they lovingly guided me back to my power. And now, in this birth, my third birth, I chose to stand alone in my truth, to trust myself, to live in this moment of almost shoulders and wait.

.... I wasn't turtle-necking him [Samuel] at the chin as I did with Grey, when the midwives knew his shoulders were lodged and took over, made me change to hands-and-knees position. From that point on, I had lost touch with Grey's head, lost touch with my birthing, while they manoeuvred his shoulders and my belly and I roared him out blindly.

I later learned from others knowledgeable about unassisted birth, and women who had birthed, without assistance, babies larger even than Grey, that the best way to birth shoulders is by simply shifting into different positions until the shoulder pops. I think it was the sitting position I was in during Grey's crowning that encouraged his shoulders to lodge. If the midwives had not suggested I lean back against George during the birth, I probably would've been squatting and better able to birth those big shoulders on my own.

But this time I was completely present and responsible; I took the squatting position as seemed natural at the time. And there was his [Samuel's] neck, ... I eventually shifted over to my left foot, putting my weight there and extending my right knee outward, just to twist my pelvis a bit, to make more room for the shoulders if necessary. ... I felt the burn of another mountain rising under my skin, a foothill. The first shoulder emerged and then the other. Yes.

"Here it comes," said Geo, as he helped my right hand support the budding body. He added, "Are you going to catch your baby?"[15]

Lay midwifery has always evolved out of community, and in the post-modern era where community has been largely lost, it may be that the role of the lay midwife is just what is needed to help bring community back to childbirth. Indeed, pockets of lay midwifery practice have existed across the industrialised world for the past 50 years regardless, from which we can draw experience. In the 1960's, the then lay birth companion Ina May Gaskin doula-ed the women of her community in learning how to support each other effectively during birth and early parenting, so that gentle birth was the norm among their mothers and caesarean birth, a tiny percentage. She teamed up with an obstetrician who was willing to teach her the medical components of her work as an apprentice midwife, so that she had the theory and practice to use if it became necessary. Once certified as a midwife, Ina May established *The Farm* birthing and midwifery centre in Tennessee and was a pioneer in getting traditional midwifery accepted as a lawful practice within the majority of States of America.[16] In Spain, the holistic pregnancy centre *Da-a-luz*, pioneered by lay midwife Vanessa Brooks, has been offering a similar safe place for the preparation of birthing families since 2001. Women are supported in their choices not only by doulas but also by midwives, both formally trained and lay, who are integrating complementary therapies, such as the use of herbs and massage, with traditional and spiritual midwifery skills.[17] The experiences of these community-based, lay-attended birthing centres, coupled with the equivalent state-provided examples already cited, already offer pointers towards a concrete prototype for future change towards mother-led childbirth.

That is not to suggest that doulas are generally frustrated midwives, or that women who work as lay supporters perpetually desire to train in and duly practice midwifery at all. The majority of doulas are doulas because they want to do what doulas do, and in the light of the supporting evidence, it seems entirely appropriate that there is always a place for the lay companion during the childbirth year. Yet I cannot help but wonder if, in the bigger picture and given the state of current world affairs, the realisation of psychosocial support for birthing families and the rise of the modern doula are not somehow timely. Lay midwife, Jeannine Parvati Baker's words *"Healing birth is healing the earth,"*[18] come to mind. It appears that a radical rethink around the way birth is 'attended' has become critical in order to ensure the protection of the continued memory of gentle physiological birth in the collective psyche of humankind. It could be said therefore, that for some women, the doula role will simply be a stepping-stone in preparation for their part in the resurrection of a traditional midwifery movement across the industrialised world.

Part Three - DOULA TALES

"Doulas typically practise whole family support. They give loving attention during the birthing time when and where it is needed and I salute them."

Patrick Houser, 2009[1]

1. Birth stories

S & C's story

"This is the birth I learnt the most from about what it actually means to be a doula, and what it means to birth consciously. For me, the story sums up how much I had to learn about trust, faith, not making assumptions and the power of female support during birth. All the things I thought I 'knew' (head-knowledge) before this birth, but which afterwards I really understood in my heart.

My lady S was nearly 2 weeks overdue and desperate to get things moving before the conversations about induction began. She had two sessions of acupuncture and did nipple stimulation and called me late Sunday night contracting 3 every 10 minutes but coping fine and would let me know when she wanted me to come. She called at 3am saying she couldn't do Reiki to herself anymore and could I come.

I arrived at 3.30 and she seemed to be cracking on, but the contractions were still quite short. I suggested hubby went to bed while she tried to sleep between contractions on the sofa with me dozing in the next room.

The midwife (MW) came around 10am to check on her. S was going to decide in labour if she wanted to go to hospital or stay at home. She decided she wanted to stay at home, so the midwife went off to organise her antibiotic injection for her Group Strep B to have in the fridge for later.

S wanted to get in the bath, so we had a lovely hour in her deep corner bath, with hubby and I pouring water over her. And things really slowed down.

By lunchtime, I think, things had picked up a bit, then died right down again. I suggested they go to bed, get a bit lovey-dovey and get some sleep and went out for a walk round their village.

I walked into the local church, which is very unusual for me, but felt the need to be somewhere quiet to reflect. I was having a major wobble - all the first time mothers I'd worked with so far had ended up with major intervention for 'failure to progress' and I

55

was terrified it was going to happen again. I texted my wonderful mentor Linda asking for ideas and she phoned me literally 2 seconds later.

She suggested some tips such as sitting backwards on a dining chair and told me in no uncertain terms that everything would be OK. This pep talk was just what I needed. I walked back and carried out Linda's suggestion and things did pick up again - contractions not more frequent, but definitely stronger.

The MW came at 4.30 again. I could tell she still considered this to be pre-labour and we all agreed then that S and hubby C needed to have something to eat and another rest.

I came home in time for me to put my kids to bed and have a bath, and she called me back about 9pm. When I got there, she was having contractions every 3/4 minutes and they were nice and long and strong. S was just using a Tens machine and her voice - she's in a choir and understands from her singing that if you tense your pelvic floor you can't sing, so she was really good at low moaning to keep everything loose.

She found that standing by her banisters was her favourite place; during a contraction she hung on and moaned or blew raspberries - she was such a star labourer!

The MW came at 10.30 again and did a VE at S's request, it was very quick because S decided it hurt too much and used midwife Mary Cronk's phrase I'd taught her - "stop that at once", so the MW got her fingers out of there pronto!

Anyway, she thought she was 5cm and fully effaced. Of course S had a wobble then. She had been contracting for nearly 24 hours and started doing that silly maths thing we do - "I've got another 24 hours to go!!!"

I told her she was on the home stretch now and just to let her body get on with the job. I had a self revelation at that point that at previous first time births I'd attended I had wobbled at this point along with the woman and that my faith in her ability to do it was not quite all there. It's one thing to say all the right words, but if you really don't have true faith, the doubts creep in and infect the atmosphere. I had an insight into what it must be like to be religious, and thought back to my time in the church earlier.

Anyway, C and I did midwife Ina May Gaskin's suggestion "shaking the apples" (holding the mother's hips between both palms and rubbing vigorously), which got her to around 8 cm pretty quickly I think.

Then I suggested a rice sock low down on her bump and she loved it! C and I had to run round putting it back in the microwave and holding it on her bump through every contraction and she freaked out if it wasn't there!

By this time the contractions were coming thick and fast and she was singing opera and marching up and down on the spot with C and I crouched on either side holding the rice sock, or wheat bag he'd found, on her bump.

The MW suggested a bath again, I felt strongly that she was 'fully' (cervix 10 centimetres dilated). As soon as she got in the bath she hated it. Got straight out and started shaking and swearing (in English by the way, which is interesting as she is French!).

I said that it was likely she was in transition and it wouldn't be long now. We went back downstairs and I just got the sense that someone needed to hold her tight. I said "give me some of that" and gathered her up in my arms through each contraction (she told me later that it really had felt as though she had 'given me some' of the pain.) Then C took over, they danced on the spot through constant contractions until finally she started grunting!

The MW looked at me and jumped up and down with thumbs up and a big smile.

The pushing urge got stronger and stronger and S fell down to hands and knees, but it didn't work that way. I suggested a supported squat as she could really bear down like that. 2nd MW arrived in time to see the head just sitting there at the perineum.

S wouldn't believe it was the head. She put her hand down and what she felt was so soft that she thought it was her bag of waters. She kept asking us to pop it so the baby could come out!

She sat on C's lap on the edge of the sofa and I whispered "just breathe him out" and slowly we saw her fan open and baby swim out, with a hand up by his face! It was 5.21am.

She wasn't even grazed.

The cord was cut after it stopped pulsating and the placenta took about an hour.

S just kept saying "Mon Deiu, I have a baby", and yes, perhaps God did have something to do with it.

That day I learnt about the importance of faith."

Contributed by **Maddie McMahon, birth and postnatal doula, Cambridge** (who 3 years later had the honour to be present at the birth of S's second baby, born in the same room, in much the same way as her big brother)

The birth of twins – in water

"I first met R after the birth (at home in water) of her first baby, to help her with breastfeeding. She contacted me again a few months ago when she became pregnant with twins to ask if I'd be their birth doula this time. She was considering another homebirth and felt she needed the support of a doula to help them navigate their way through the system. I was delighted of course, but also apprehensive as although I had experience of working with twins postnatally, I had not had experience of a twin birth. We chatted about them also making contact with another doula colleague who had more experience than I, not only with twins but in having good connections at their chosen hospital and probably more clout than me when it came down to getting their birth plan adhered to, which I felt was going to take some doing! Doula H was happy to help but already had holidays planned, so, with R and T's agreement, H and I arranged to support them on a shared care basis. We attended the antenatal meetings together and the long on call period of 8 weeks and during this time R had many meetings with her midwives and consultant, trying to pave the way for the natural birth they so wanted.

After much deliberation, R and T did agree to have a hospital birth providing that they could use the midwife led unit (MLU) once she got past 36 weeks if all remained well. They remained steadfast in their desire for a natural birth, and managed to get their birth plan ok'd by the head of midwifery and consultant and circulated to the supervisors of midwives (SOM)! This included: only midwives, husband and doula to be present during labour and birth, no cannula, no continuous monitoring, opportunity to labour in water, no pain relief to be offered, quiet environment with minimum disturbance for at least 15 mins after birth of first baby to give contractions opportunity to re-start naturally for birth of second baby - thereafter options for aiding contractions to be discussed, no Vitamin K, no paediatricians to be present during birth unless babies premature or showing signs of distress, routine paediatric checks to take place after adequate skin to skin and breastfeeding time.

Well, the 36 week milestone came and went, as did 37, 38 and 39 weeks! The more time went on the more anxious H and I became that R's birth plan may get eroded with pressure being put on her for induction. R was becoming more uncomfortable and suffering with symphysis pubis dysfunction and at 38+5 weeks she agreed to a gentle membrane sweep after which she was told she was already 3-4 cm dilated. Almost a week later (Thursday) she called me to say her routine CTG had been fine but that the midwives wanted to see her again after the weekend to weigh up her options. Later that day she had a show however, and as H was now on holiday, I very much prepared myself for a call over the weekend. R was in good spirits and seemed calmer and more relaxed.

I was woken in the early hours of Saturday morning at 4.30am by T calling me to say that R's waters had gone an hour before, that contractions had started and they were about to make their way to the hospital. I arrived at the MLU at 5.10am to find R being assessed by the midwife (N). Twins were fine and R was now contracting 4 in ten lasting approx 45 seconds, breathing beautifully through them and asking for the pool to be filled. T was massaging R's lower back during contractions and the ambience in the room was calm and quiet. N said she would need to do a VE 'to see if she was in labour' (we couldn't help but chuckle) after which she looked surprised to find her already 9cm dilated! (Actually, I could understand how the midwife may have wanted 'proof' of labour because R was managing her contractions so well that you really couldn't tell if they were painful!) R then politely refused any more monitoring or disturbance and N respectfully obliged. We were quickly moved to the room with the pool and R got into the water at 6pm. I dimmed the lights, T put the music on and very shortly afterwards R said to me 'I think I need to push, should I?', so I encouraged her to just let her body take over and go with it, no need for 'pushing' just to breath through it. N was not present at that time and R was calmly 'getting on with it'. But at 6.14am, when the first baby's head appeared, I ran to get N! She arrived with the second midwife and their SOM, and at 6.16am, Baby A was born serenely in the water with R guiding her up to her chest where she said hello to this beautiful calm baby, no fuss, no crying, everyone in hushed voices just admiring the scene.

The cord was clamped and cut at 6.22am and Baby A was handed over to dad for some skin to skin while R got on with birthing baby two. The SOM suggested that they break her waters to help with getting the contractions starting again but we asked for a few minutes to 'wait and see'. I put a drop of Clary Sage on a flannel for R to breathe and within a couple of minutes contractions had started again and she felt the baby moving down. At 6.27am twin two's head emerged with the amniotic sac still intact and at 6.29am she was born in the caul! R guided Baby M up to her to say hello, and I got to hold Baby A while R and T had a few precious minutes with Baby M, waiting for the third stage. Another very calm birth with no fuss, no crying, but after a couple of minutes the MW gently rubbed her to stimulate her to take her first breath. There was no urgency as the cord was still attached so she was getting oxygen, but they just gently massaged her and she started breathing and murmuring while gazing at her mum. (NB. no paeds!)

When the placenta started to come away there was a fair amount of blood loss, so syntometrine was given (with consent) and the placenta was delivered at 6.39am. All appeared fine and R got out of the pool, exhausted but ecstatically happy and she rested on the bed for a little while and I got her and T some tea and cereal.

Within the hour, at R's request, I placed first one, then the other baby, near her breasts where they self attached and fed avidly for 40 minutes with R lying back in the biological nurturing position. Simply amazing to watch! All three midwives kept congratulating R and saying how amazing it had been, saying how much they admired her for having the courage of her convictions to birth the babies naturally. They commented that they so very rarely see births like this, that most twin births go straight to caesarean section and the ones that do birth vaginally are very much 'managed'.

At about 9am T helped R to get showered and I tidied up the room. Babies were checked over: A weighed in at 7lb 3oz and M 6lb 15oz. I helped the family get settled, we talked over her amazing birth once more and then I left them in peace (with a hopeful 6 hour discharge). I know this was a special experience but really I can't help feeling it was just a natural birth, the same as every other except with two babies!"

Contributed by Bev Mills-Ashwell, birth and postnatal doula, Surrey.

A refugee mother's story

"When the Sure Start midwife introduced us, all I knew about my new client was that she was 23 years old, from the Congo, her parents had been murdered when she was 13, she had been married off very young and it was an abusive marriage, she was pregnant as the result of having been raped by a group of soldiers, and she had been in the UK for 2 months. Also she spoke no English. She had had no antenatal education and was understandably very scared.

I put my numbers in her mobile phone although I had no idea how we would speak to each other if she rang! I visited her with the intention of packing a hospital bag but when we went to go through her belongings, it became obvious that she didn't have anything to pack and didn't even have a bag. I went home and put together a bag, my old dressing gown, and a front opening nightdress borrowed from my mother. My concern was that because of what had happened to her she would not feel able to go into labour and would end up having a very invasive medicalised birth. I was determined to try and prevent that at all costs because of the risk of triggering PTSD if she found herself held down and powerless while other people did things to her. She was already suffering flashbacks of the rape.

A few days later I took her to an appointment at the mental health services perinatal unit. She was under their care with the intention of having her as an inpatient after the baby was born if there were any problems with bonding. They had arranged an interpreter and through her I gave my client a crash course in what happens in labour. I demonstrated positions and stressed the need to keep active. I went through the pain relief options and she was adamant she didn't want any injections or an epidural. I explained to her that if she had a caesarean section either the interpreter or I would be with her in theatre. Finally, I asked the interpreter to tell her that she was very brave, she was strong, she should trust in her body and she will be able to birth this baby. And that I would be there for her all the way through it and afterwards.

To my total surprise my phone rang at 11.30 that night and a little voice said in French "cinque minutes". She meant she was having contractions every five minutes. When I arrived at her flat she was panicking. I encouraged her into the bath with the lights off and just a light on in another room. She immediately calmed down as I sat on the loo and held her hand and stroked her legs to encourage her to relax. We stayed like that for about two hours and then we ran out of hot water. By this time the contractions were coming every 3 minutes but she was still calm and coping well. I rang the delivery suite and said she was in labour and explained the situation to them. I said that she must not be examined if it could be avoided, people must not crowd around her, she should not be held down in any way, and no one must touch her at all without her permission. She stayed calm despite having a male paramedic in uniform near her in the ambulance. (Men in uniform were a flashpoint for her panics.)

I asked if she could go in the pool as she had done so well in the bath at home but the midwife said not unless she was 5cms dilated and she would have to examine her to check. We decided to wait until the interpreter arrived to explain the VE situation and give her the choice as to whether she wanted it or not. Meanwhile the baby was monitored while she stood up.

The interpreter arrived and explained to her she could not go in the pool without having a VE and she agreed to it. That was the only VE she had. She was 5cms so she got straight into the pool where she stayed for a couple of hours. Eventually she decided she wanted to get out although the midwife was happy for her to have a water birth. When she had a contraction she rocked on the spot, walked, or held on to me. She had no pain relief. I did try a wheat bag and massage but she preferred to be active and mobile. We kept the lights very low and tried to make her feel as safe as possible. The midwife was very hands off just coming in every 15 minutes to check the baby. If she stayed in the room she sat quietly on the floor out of the way and left us to it. My client started making pushy noises and eventually went onto the floor on all fours.

At about 7am she birthed her baby daughter on the floor, on the mat with her back against a beanbag. I sat next to her with my arm round her and holding her hand. She looked very shocked and started to cry. I was worried that reality would hit home now and she would push the baby away but when the midwife asked if she wanted her on her tummy she said yes and held out her arms. She had a natural third stage and the placenta came out very quickly. She held her baby skin to skin throughout it all.

I left her in bed wearing my mother's nightdress and my old dressing gown still holding her baby - looking a bit shell-shocked but happy.

She breastfed and bonded well with her daughter which was a relief given the circumstances of her pregnancy. She stayed under the care of the mental health unit although was not on medication or an inpatient. They discharged her after a few weeks and were amazed at how well she was doing. I saw her nearly every day and took her to register the birth, made appointments with her solicitor for the asylum process and got emergency payments from the Home Office after her money was stopped while she was in hospital.

Thinking about it afterwards, I definitely think that encouraging her to trust her body and know that I was there for her perhaps gave her the cue to let go and have the baby. Then when she went into labour I just made her safe, dark little spaces and growled protectively (in a friendly way!) if anyone came near her."

Contributed by Lesley Hilton, birth and postnatal doula, Leeds area

Chris and Claire's story: from a father's perspective

"At first, I was unsure about having a doula. After all, isn't birth meant to be a private and intimate experience for a woman and her husband? A special moment together welcoming their baby into the world? Why involve others?

However, after speaking to a couple of work colleagues, I found that my ideal 'private birth' was not very near to reality. One colleague's wife laboured for 36 hours, altogether supported by 3 different midwives during labour, with 7 members of hospital staff in the room for a failed instrumental delivery, and the same again in theatre for a caesarean section. Another, though more straightforward, still involved a large amount of hospital staff ending with 3 midwives, a student and a doctor present at an assisted delivery.

We thought long and hard about what we should do to try and avoid the situations I had been talking about, and to try to achieve the 'perfect birth'. We finally decided Claire would aim for a home birth, possibly with the help of a doula. Claire had been reading about doulas in one of the many pregnancy books she had acquired, and then the subject was brought up again at our NCT classes. It seemed to make sense. A professional birth support partner could help us through the whole experience, making a natural birth more likely, and making the labour easier not just for Claire, but for me too! I read up about it and found research stating how having the additional support of a doula could reduce the chance of a c-section by 50%, reduce the likelihood of medical interventions and shorten the length of labour by 25%. Great! I thought, but it did all sound a little too good to be true.

We rung 3 doulas up, thinking we'd make a decision after seeing them as to whether we needed a doula or not, and arranged to meet them all. We met Jayn first, and we chatted for nearly 2 hours about what we wanted, about our hopes and fears for the birth, and about how she may be able to help us. We all instantly hit it off with each other. She was so, well, likeable, so down to earth, and so knowledgeable about the whole birthing process. Everything she said made so much sense. As our meeting drew to an end, Jayn mentioned it may be good to see another doula, possibly 2 to make sure we got someone we were completely comfortable with, who we'd be happy to be at the birth of our 1st baby. However, the look on Claire's face, as we shut the door to Jayn, said it all. She beamed at me saying 'She is the one! We don't need to see the other doulas, I want her there!!' I had to agree, she was perfect for us.

In the weeks that followed, Claire met up with Jayn twice more, they went through Claire's birth plan together, and chatted about the pregnancy, the upcoming birth, and looking after new babies. Claire found the meetings so helpful. She had been slightly nervous about the birth, but seemed to be getting less nervous and more excited. This was more noticeable after each of the meet-ups with our doula. Jayn put Claire at great ease about it all. They kept in regular contact by email and telephone.

Two days before the due date, Claire got up in the morning and had a show. The first thing she did was to ring Jayn, who assured her that all was OK, and told her things may start, but it was also possible that they wouldn't for another day or 2. As it was Claire started having niggling pains a couple of hours afterwards.

We just chilled out together for a few hours, with the pains becoming more strong, and getting closer together. We rung Jayn and the midwives to let them know what was happening. At about 11 o' clock, I rung Jayn saying perhaps she could make her way round, the contractions were getting stronger, and we could do with the extra support. Jayn was with us within the hour, and on arriving gave us both a big hug, (Claire told me afterwards how much this meant to her, and how she felt more relaxed knowing someone was there to look after us both!). Her waters broke at about 1.15, and then things really seemed to hot up. Jayn and I took it in turns to be with Claire, sorting out the oil burner, the music, and rubbing her back or supporting her through contractions, getting her water to sip, and just being there for whatever she wanted. At just before 3 we rung the midwives again, saying we would like someone to come out, at this point Claire seemed to be in a world of her own. As soon as I had put the phone down, Claire said she needed to push, and got quite upset. Jayn comforted her, and told her not to worry, but to just go with what her body was telling her to do. I became concerned at this stage that the baby might arrive before the midwife, but Jayn seemed very calm and this reassured me.

The midwife arrived about 25 minutes after we called, and when she arrived, she called for the second midwife, but it seemed Claire was intent on doing the birth as privately as possible as was our initial intention, as she pushed the baby out before the support midwife arrived. It was a beautiful (or should I say handsome) baby boy. What a fantastic, emotional moment it was, and to be honest, I don't think I would have noticed if there were fifty people in the room. That moment was just Claire's and mine, with our new son.

After congratulating us, Jayn retreated, and went and sat quietly on the other side of the room. Sid tucked into mummy Claire for a really good breastfeed, and then after an hour or so was weighed and checked over by the second midwife. The midwives left us at around 5, and Jayn did some tidying, made us some sandwiches and a lovely cup of tea. All was calm in the Connell household, and after Claire had had a shower, and got into bed, Jayn left, saying just call if there was anything we needed to ask her. Again what reassurance - she was just at the end of the phone.

We were over the moon with the complete birth experience, it really couldn't have been better. Claire was elated after the birth (I expected her to be exhausted) but she was so happy, and so pleased with the birth, and with our lovely Sid. We were and still are so grateful to Jayn, she helped us really achieve the birth we wanted, she kept us calm, she was comforting and reassuring, and just what we needed. We had a private, drug free, intervention free wonderful birth experience, exactly the way we wanted. Now how many people can say that?"

Written by Chris Connell (husband to Claire, father to Sid). Contributed by Jayn Stapleton, birth doula, West Sussex

J & A's story

"*8.30am* A calls to say that J has been up all night having irregular contractions, can't lie down as too painful.

1pm I call for an update, J is in bath. We talk and her contractions sound strong but still not regular. I offer to come but they are coping and about to have lunch.

5pm Contractions are regular every 10 minutes. They ask me to come.

7pm I arrive after what is normally a 25 minute drive that takes me 2 hours as traffic is horrendous. Contractions are every 5 minutes, lasting about 30 seconds. J cannot sit or lie down as too uncomfortable so she is pacing the house and I notice she is twisting her hands and wrists a lot. She also clicks her fingers and shakes her wrists during some contractions. She has an isolated pain down one side of her back that seems to be giving her constant aggravation. She thinks it may be a twisted muscle.

A decides that now I am here he will go to Comet and buy a CD player for going to hospital. This is the first of his many disappearances throughout the labour.

8.25pm J has started taking Arnica, I have turned off the TV and the lights and we are in candlelight in the quiet. She is pacing the house going from living room to loo, she is tired but still can't manage to sit or lie down. We try kneeling on the floor over the couch and leaning on me. I rub her back and her breathing is excellent. Really deep and slow. We get to know each other over the next few hours and as we are alone we build up a good rapport and trust.

9pm Nothing is comfortable any more so I suggest a bath. Get J all comfy and she relaxes. A is eating pizza downstairs. J starts to throw up. I grab a bucket and after some time she feels much better.

10.30pm J asks to go to hospital. We get her out the bath and dressed and pack up.

11.30pm Arrive at hospital. Midwife (MW) takes one look at us and rushes us to a delivery room. A retreats into himself and although I am rather aware it is not the 'done thing', I end up having to introduce them to the MW and update her with the story so far. MW (N) is an older experienced African lady. J describes her to me as "like a teacher" when she is out the room. She is strict, she has little time for niceties and gives precise instructions. Put the elastic belt on, get her gown on etc. She does the usual checks and then a vaginal examination (VE) which shows J to be 3-4 centimetres dilated (A vanishes before examination is done). J is put on a monitor. As she is finding it very hard to sit or lie down this makes it all worse. N suggests an epidural. Tells J they are great, they take away all the pain and last the whole labour until pushing. J needs little persuasion and has explicitly told me in our meeting she had every intention of using one and has a low pain threshold. We have to wait for an anaesthetist as he is doing a caesarean section (c/s). I ask N why the constant monitoring is necessary as J is so uncomfortable with her back and she explains it is for litigation reasons, as they will have a print out of everything throughout the labour. She then relents and says she supposes she can do it manually and I ask if she could also locate a birth ball to try. I put on the CD player and J chooses a CD of Kenyan gospel music. N suggests trying Entonox whilst we wait for epidural and within 3 contractions J is a changed woman.

1.45am J is standing and dancing and singing (when she can!) along to the hymns. She goes totally into herself and is oblivious to me & N who watches her in awe. A arrives back to this brilliant scene. N relaxes with us now and turns out to be a really lovely lady. We talk about all sorts of things quietly whilst J labours with her music. N's shift ends at 8am and she is sure she will be here to deliver if things continue as they are.

2.15am Female anaesthetist arrives. Highly experienced lady in her 50's. However, Venflon fails twice and then has to be put in the other wrist. J complains bitterly at the pain it causes her. Epidural put in.

2.55am Epidural is working. J back on bed with monitor on. She is denied food although she is hungry so she rests. I am still optimistic at this point.

4am VE shows J is 4-5 centimetres dilated. N suggests an artificial rupture of membranes (ARM) to speed things up a bit. We all discuss and decide ok. N tries but cant do it.

4.45am Syntocinon drip started. N takes her break.

5am A tiny but absolutely terrifying Chinese lady bursts into the room. She announces herself to be the Sister in Charge and informs J that she does not usually take on "cases" but has to as it is "so crazy out there" (in the rest of labour ward). She looks at the notes and starts shouting at us that it is RIDICULOUS that J has an epidural while her waters are still intact. I try to explain that N did try but couldn't which sets her off more and she goes berserk that N should have told her that she couldn't do it. With no further ado, no permission asked or discussion had, she pulls up J's knees, tells her to relax and does an ARM. Once finished she says that she also decided to have a good sweep around and that J was now 6cm.

I am totally horrified at the whole scene almost not believing that my client has just been treated like a cat at the vet. A is not there to witness. She then dismisses J taking the Arnica and says she saw no need or reason for it and to just get on with it. J rolls her eyes at me and says to me later that she saw "no point in arguing with a woman like that".

6.45am A is back and snoring in a chair. He went home at some stage during the night but didn't tell us that he was planning to. His   hr trips to the car park have also meant that I have been unable to leave J or have any break aside from a 10 second wee for fear of leaving her alone or her being manhandled by another MW. I am fading fast.

8.00am N finishes her shift and new MW (C) takes over – very young, bubbly, enthusiastic - and K who is a student MW in her 40's, an enlightened lady who has been working as an antenatal & postnatal teacher for years and has studied with Michel Odent and Active Birth pioneers.

9.20am Dr comes in & decides to increase the syntocinon.

9.30am VE finds J to be 8 centimetres dilated but there is fresh meconium on her sanitary pad. Baby is happy & heart rate is fine so they are not worried.

10.20am Epidural wearing off and not working. Turns out there is a blood clot in the tube. Anaesthetist says he will have to take it out and re-do from scratch but first has to do all the planned c/s of the day. J goes back to using the Entonox and waits.

11.45am Epidural re-done by brilliantly efficient, pleasant and super speedy anaesthetist.

12.20pm VE = 9½ centimetres

12.45pm Dr arrives. She is a very harassed white Jamaican lady with no time for bedside manner. I overheard her on the phone outside complaining that she had to leave this hospital at 1pm to be at another one. She tells C that she wants another VE done an hour from the last one (at 1.20pm) and if J is not 10 centimetres dilated and baby in a good position then she is' sectioning' her. J bursts into shocked tears at hearing this. K the student MW's jaw actually drops. No preamble, no warning, just this statement out of the blue. Not even really directed at J. Dr leaves and the baby's heart rate drops. MW immediately goes back to get her. She rushes back in and says that it is a normal reaction to the syntocinon boost and not to worry.

1pm Baby's heart rate is dropping each time there is a contraction. MW thinks it is a good sign that the baby's head is coming down and being squashed each time, but goes to get Dr again anyway.

1.10pm Dr returns. Decides to VE herself. There is fresh meconium again on her gloves and J's cervix is still 9 centimetres dilated. She says that they are now forcing out a baby that doesn't want to come and she is not happy with the heart rate at all. She declares an emergency c/s.

Things are very rushed now, Dr leaves and a different one comes in to explain the procedure. J is frightened & shocked and exhausted. A decides to stick around and go to theatre and goes to change into scrubs and I stay close to J and try to be of some comfort.

A different MW sweeps into the room. She is loud, mouthy, brusque, offhand and obscenely rude. In the midst of this upset she stands on one side of the bed and actually starts to shout at J telling her to "SIT UP, SIT UP, MOVE BACK, NOT LIKE THAT, MOVE YOUR BUM BACK". I am standing on the opposite side absolutely FURIOUS that she is shouting at my client at all but especially considering the circumstances. I try to keep calm and help J to sit up and within minutes she is wheeled off. I am left standing in the now empty room and I break down through exhaustion, shock and upset. K the student MW sees me and quickly comes back. She gives me a huge hug and says that she would really like to reflect with me once this is over as she feels similar disappointment about this case. I wait in the delivery room and try to compose myself for the parent's return.

J returns an hour later with a 6lb baby girl. She has a very elongated head that they have cleverly disguised in a pink knitted hat! She is really yelling and putting her tiny fist in her mouth and sucking like mad. J is quiet and stunned. A goes off to change out of scrubs and "freshen up". He doesn't return for 40 minutes.

The MW (C) tells me that the baby was OP and had a deflexed head so there was "no way" she could have delivered her naturally. I politely ask her if she had not realised the position when she palpated J when her shift began. She said that she had had a hunch because of the backache, the slow progress and on feeling the baby, but had decided not to say anything to J as it wouldn't have changed the outcome anyway. I nodded, but inside I was a knotted ball. Am I wrong in thinking that surely it is J's baby and J's body and she has a RIGHT to know?

J asks if I want to hold the baby. I do want to, but A hasn't held her yet so I decline and tell her she probably wants to be with her mummy for the time being. I help her to feed along with K the student MW and then once A returns I leave. I can feel that I am on the verge of really breaking down and I don't want J or A to see me upset. They thank me and A wants to take lots of pictures. As I get into the lift, student MW K follows me in and walks me to my car. She says that she had to leave after the c/s and go outside to cry as she was so appalled by what she had seen today and said that she was so glad I was there as it made her feel like her feelings were validated - she could tell by my reaction that she was not the only one who thought that what had happened was outrageous. She said she had been at this hospital for 7 weeks and wanted to go home and never return. She had seen section after section and few women allowed to attempt to birth their babies. I really felt for her as she is so clearly in her job for all the right reasons and feels impotent because of her position.

I leave at about 4.15 pm.

I think this was by far the steepest learning curve in my doula training so far. It took me to the edge and made me question if I could continue as a doula and if I had a similar experience again, whether I would be able to cope. It traumatised me to know that there are MWs and Drs in the system who behave like this on a day-to-day basis and it is considered ok. I was not myself for 2 days afterwards. I was devastated. I cried, I was angry, I was totally physically & emotionally exhausted. I also had a deep feeling of disappointment that I had failed to protect J and that I had therefore failed as a doula. After time and lots of reflecting with my mentor, I made peace with this experience, but it is a birth I will never forget for all the wrong reasons."

Contributed by Lauren Mishcon, birth doula, London

Jane's birth: I can do this!

"As a doula, it's impossible to say whether births are 'good' or 'bad', never mind singling one out as the 'best' birth ever. However, if it's possible to have a perfect doula experience, then the first home birth I attended comes pretty close.

'Jane' had already attempted a home birth several years previously: she had laboured well for hours, until the midwives in attendance became concerned by her apparent lack of progress and insisted on a transfer to hospital. Once at the hospital,

Jane was told by the consultant that if she didn't give birth within the hour, she'd be going under the knife. Tall, strong, flame-haired Jane wasn't going to give in that easily: with a few almighty pushes, she gave birth to a beautiful daughter. The doctor muttered something about Jane's 'in-coordinate uterus' and suggested that she forget about having any future births at home.

By the time Jane contacted me, she was about halfway through her second pregnancy, and was determined to prove that doctor wrong. She was still outraged by her treatment at the hospital, and although it was clear that she believed in the power of normal birth, her confidence had undoubtedly taken a knock. I wasn't sure whether I was the right person to support Jane – as a new doula, I had only ever attended one other birth, which had ended in a forceps delivery that I hadn't even been 'allowed' into theatre to witness, and my own daughter's birth had ended in a caesarean section – but in the end, Jane had more faith in me than I had in myself. 'Just the fact that you're on this path to being a doula means that your heart is in the right place,' Jane told me over the phone. 'I trust you.' I made a silent promise to myself that I would honour Jane's faith in my commitment.

Over the course of Jane's pregnancy, we met several times to discuss the previous birth and to explore her choices for the next one. During these meetings, Jane's daughter would flit around the room, sipping a beaker of pressed apple juice while her favourite Pingu cartoon played on a permanent loop on the TV. Jane and I struck up an easy friendship; I felt honoured to be part of her family at such a special time.

Jane was reading Gowri Motha's 'Gentle Birth Method', whose emphasis on Ayurvedic nurturing and holistic wellness gave her a framework for her antenatal preparation. Motha also recommends a regular course of massage, so Jane, her husband and I paid a visit to a local massage therapist who specialises in massage for the childbearing year. Together, we learned some strokes and techniques that might benefit Jane in labour – little did I know how useful that hour-long session would prove to be.

As Jane's due date came and went, her chances of getting that longed-for home birth appeared to wane rapidly. She received (and deflected) the usual pressure to be induced as time passed by. The hospital's community midwives had only agreed to be on call for two weeks after Jane's due date, and when I woke up on day 14 with no sign of Jane, I feared that things might slip out of her control. However, at six o'clock that evening, Jane's husband 'Ted' called. The sound of a client's partner's voice over the phone is always thrilling: it's a sure sign that the client herself is 'indisposed' – too focused on early labour to speak. Ted told me that he and Jane had gone for a long *walk in the woods that day (quite an achievement for a heavily pregnant woman in the middle of a frozen February), and that things seemed to be starting off. He told me he'd ring back when they wanted me to come. I remember hurtling delightedly around the house for a while, packing my doula bag with the precision of a novice, until Ted phoned again an hour later and asked me to come along.*

When I pulled up outside Jane's little stone cottage, a warm yellow light spilled from the windows. What a difference from the harsh fluorescent glare of the hospital. I bounded up the steps, and when Ted opened the door, I had to do that instant downshift in mood that comes when one enters a birth space: my excitement was barely containable, but the mood inside the cottage was still and serene. I walked into the bedroom and Jane was a vision of strength: rocking gently on her birth ball, wearing an oversized green T-shirt that made her ginger hair seem all the more fiery, eyes closed, listening to Holst's 'Planets' on her earphones. Jane was already on her way to Labourland: she opened her eyes and chatted amiably when I came in, but it was clear that her voyage had begun.

The next four hours were a textbook lesson in normal birth: I pulled up a chair behind Jane and began to apply some of the massage strokes we'd learned a few weeks earlier, and as minutes melted into each other, it was clear from Jane's demeanour that her contractions were quickly intensifying. She went from bouncing on the ball, to leaning over the bed, to leaning against the wall, in that restless labour dance, and all the while I shadowed her, my hands on her sacrum, easing oils over her hips. Ted phoned the hospital and a midwife arrived just before midnight – Jane's impeccable timing meant that she'd get a shot at that home birth, after all.

In the final throes of her labour, Jane knelt on the living room floor and gripped a wooden chair in front of her. At her back, my forearms burned from four hours of solid massage, but the minute I stopped my work, Jane's cries of 'Leah! Don't stop!' drew me back. Ted was by her head, supporting her with his quiet, steady love, whispering words of encouragement. As Jane's groans turned to grunts, it was clear that the baby wasn't far away.

'I can do this! I can do this! I CAN DO THIS!' shouted Jane. My joy in that moment, my pride in Jane, my pride in women, were boundless. 'You ARE doing it!', I responded, as the baby's head slipped smoothly out. For one fantastically long, still minute, the baby's head stayed there, and I saw that baby's 'original face': beautiful, glowing, motionless. One more push and a baby boy came sliding out. Jane had done it, and I had witnessed my first completely normal birth: well, as 'normal' as such an extraordinary and triumphant achievement could ever be.

As Jane (tear-free) settled in to feed her baby and deliver her placenta, I decided to give her some space, so I went into the bathroom to prepare a candlelit bath. I wanted to honour Jane for what she had done: for her faith in me, and for her faith in herself. I've attended many births since Jane's, both at home and in the hospital, but that vision of Jane – she of the 'in-coordinate uterus' – pushing her baby out and shouting 'I can do it!' will stay with me forever.

A little epilogue: several years after that experience, I was on all fours in my own bedroom, just a few pushes away from the home birth of my second child. The labour had progressed at warp speed, and it was clear that the midwives would not arrive in time to give me a whiff of gas and air, let alone catch the baby. As I hunkered down, bit my pillow, and roared my way through the final throes of my daughter's birth, Jane's words rang in my head: 'I can do this!' And I did."

Contributed by Leah Hazard, birth and postnatal doula, Glasgow. Author of *The Father's Home Birth Handbook*.

2. Postnatal stories

An anonymous mother's story

"I once was called by a woman who was pregnant with her first child. She sounded very nice on the phone but scared and nervous. We chatted for a while and arranged a time for me to go and meet her.

A few days later when she opened her front door to me, she saw my smiling face and burst into tears. Her story came tumbling out with hardly a space to take a breath. She was having a dreadful pregnancy; feeling unwell, emotionally unstable, fearful of the birth, but most of all, fearful of motherhood. She seemed to dread having the baby, despite it being a much longed for, planned pregnancy. She was convinced that she would not bond with the baby, be disgusted by the birth process and afraid of the intimate bodily contact that motherhood would entail. She felt she would be a less than perfect mother and feared her inability to do things perfectly. These feelings were strong and obviously truthful, but I did not probe her at all to find out why she had these troubling thoughts.

She told me she wanted the baby taken away, cleaned and wrapped before seeing her. She did not want to hold the baby until she said so. She did not want to breastfeed. She told me her midwife had looked shocked, then laughed and said "you'll feel different after the birth". She asked me if I thought her a monster.

Quite by chance I had only just been reading some work by Reva Rubin, a Nurse Theorist who details the normal instinctive behaviours of new mothers towards their newborns. I explained to my client about how mothers need a number of things to progress healthily through the transition to parenthood, to ensure the 'safe passage' of the infant. Planning her labour helps make the birth real in her mind and helps her connect with her unborn child. Mothers need to seek acceptance of themselves in the role of mother and seek acceptance from others for the infant. I mentioned that us mothers only have to be good enough, not perfect - that we need support and validation by family, friends and society as we grow into mothers and we need others to worship our beautiful newborns to help us see them as they truly are.

I then told her that Rubin had observed that women who birth with minimal observation and intervention often do not scoop their babies to the breast immediately after the birth. They look at the baby first, taking in the miracle before them then progress to touching with fingertips, then palms of the hands and only then taking the infant into their embrace and establishing eye contact. I told her that she could wait to see how she felt after the birth. That there was no one 'right way' to greet her child and that I would support her unconditionally whatever she planned beforehand, or however she felt along the way.

She cried with relief and said she had thought she was crazy.

It turned out that I saw a lot of this client during her pregnancy, gently helping her to talk to her unborn daughter and plan her birth. She planned to go to hospital as soon as she had contractions and request an epidural and to bottle-feed her daughter expressed milk as much as she was able. I accepted those decisions unconditionally.

When she went into labour, I went to her house. She seemed happy to stay at home for a while. Her husband was calm and unfazed and he and I kept her distracted until she felt she needed to go to hospital. I thought she was about half way to fully dilated and on examination she was 6cm and fully effaced. She had her epidural and an eventual forceps delivery - she had called the shots the whole way through and seemed happy to have had her baby vaginally.

After the birth, her husband and I laid her wrapped newborn on the bed between her legs and watched in awe as she went through all the steps I had described to her. To read a book is one thing, but to see it in action is quite another - she took a few minutes to touch her sleeping newborn and progressed slowly until, with a whoop of joy, she gathered her daughter in her arms, looked up at us and laughed at our tear-stained faces.

Working with this lady in the postnatal period was another challenge. She still struggled with her need for perfection and her anxiety about 'getting things right'. But it was obvious her love for her daughter grew every day. She resisted my suggestion of bathing together as a way to cope with the difficult evenings alone (her husband worked long hours) with a baby who was very unsettled in the early evenings. I could see the idea of skin-to-skin contact with the baby was a difficult one for her.

However, one morning I arrived when her baby was around 6 weeks old. She opened the door to me with a strange smile on her face. Apparently the night before, in desperation with a screaming baby, she ran a warm bath, stripped herself and her daughter and got in. She held her purple, bawling infant to her chest and peace descended. Closing her eyes in blessed relief, she lay with her child in silence for around 10 minutes. She was aware her daughter was wiggling around a little and allowed her to move around on the safe confines of her chest. Suddenly she felt a strange sensation, opened her eyes and looked down to see her baby suckling contentedly!

This client didn't have a euphoric natural birth, or end up exclusively breastfeeding. She never really liked feeding her daughter at the breast but she could see how much her baby enjoyed it. She therefore allowed her to nurse once or twice a day for the next several months.

I look back on this client often. She reminds me of the small, everyday miracles that doulas witness when we can offer completely non-judgemental support and remain a benign presence in the background. We do not have a starring role in the drama that is a new family finding its feet. We can't always have clients who parent the way we think best; but we can have the deep faith that enables us to believe that almost all parents come to love their babies - and that really, all babies need is love."

Contributed by Maddie McMahon, birth and postnatal doula

C's story

"C was 25 with learning difficulties. She lived a fairly independent life in a flat provided for her but could only do so if she kept to a strict routine. Although she could read and write she was unable to really understand what she was reading. She reacted badly to people visiting unexpectedly and had to have things written in her diary, although even then she usually forgot them. Her flat was clean and tidy and she was fiercely proud of her possessions. The Argos catalogue was her bible. She managed her money well by strictly allocating set amounts each week for each necessity. Whenever she went shopping she would take her shopping trolley and would not go out until she had spent ages gelling her fringe down, tying a bandana over her head, and finishing it off with a black woolly hat. (She wore all of that in labour and I knew things were progressing when she took off the woolly hat!)

She had family living locally but was not on good terms with her alcoholic mother, her brother was in prison, and her grandmother (who she was close to) had cancer and was quite unwell and unable to help her much. Unfortunately her grandmother had also instilled in C the idea that the health and social services would like to take her baby away from her.

Our first meeting was less than promising. I went with the Sure Start midwife to meet her and she refused to open the door. "F**k off, I'm cooking my dinner!" came through the letterbox. Eventually she did open the door but only to hurl a torrent of abuse at the midwife. Finally she looked at me and said, "You can come in but not her." We explained that it was both of us or nothing at this stage and eventually were allowed in. Since then, I learned that although the statutory workers obviously had to treat her with kid gloves, my best way of getting her to interact constructively with me was to play her at her own game. Hence the expression "C, stop p*****g about and just get on with it" became a standard part of my interactions with her!

It has to be said that by her own admission she loved sex. Or as she used to put it, "I love my nooky!", usually said at the top of her voice. She had got pregnant with a boy with whom she had a stormy on-off relationship. I felt that although he welcomed the idea of the baby he had no commitment to C and merely used her for sex and for somewhere to sleep when he didn't want to go home.

She had the baby in hospital after being induced. It was a fast labour and she coped well only needing gas and air. However she tore badly as he came out as she found it impossible to stop pushing when the midwife asked her to, and had to go to theatre for a third degree tear to be repaired. The baby appeared in good condition at birth but then immediately stopped breathing and had to be resuscitated. C was unaware of this as, at the time, she was on her mobile phone!

I went to pick her up from hospital about 4 days after the birth. She didn't want to go home saying she loved it there and in particular liked the food. Eventually I managed to get her out and into the car and took them back to her flat and settled them in. The boyfriend, having promised to come and help, was nowhere to be found and eventually I rang him and told him in no uncertain terms to come and help her as I did not think she should be on her own with a newborn baby the first night home.

One of the biggest problems we had was trying to find creative ways of getting her to take the medication she had been sent home with. Because she had a third degree tear she had about 6 sorts of drugs to take at different intervals each day. Painkillers, antibiotics, laxatives, iron etc. Whatever we tried – charts, lists – nothing worked and she was completely confused. Eventually I hit on the idea of going to her flat with a pile of envelopes and emptying all the tablets out and putting them in each envelope with the time and day written on the outside, then bundling them up in date order, with strict instructions to throw away each envelope as she used it. It worked reasonably well but it took us several days to establish the routine. I was concerned that the hospital had sent someone with learning difficulties home knowing she lived on her own and expecting her to take so many drugs with such a complicated regime.

She breastfed really well although she had bought bottles and a steriliser before the birth. After a couple of days she had sore nipples. I suggested the usual things but she insisted on using the pump and would not listen to alternatives. I showed her how to use the sterilizer.

The next day she announced she wanted to stop breastfeeding as she was "fed up with it." I suggested as she was doing so well that she kept going for a few more days as it was better for the baby. However I had concerns about how often she was feeding him as, once, when I suggested that he was hungry she replied that she had already fed him – but she couldn't remember when. I think she was unprepared for the amount of feeds he needed and because she had no real concept of time, could not keep track of it all. So in her head she had already fed him once that day and that was enough.

She used to ring me all the time. These calls could range from "I've just eaten a Pot Noodle and thrown up!" to "I've had a row with my boyfriend" to "The baby's gone blue!" One weekend she phoned me 30 times.

One day I arrived and found her in tears. She said her stitches and her nipples hurt. She wanted to start bottle feeding but her boyfriend wanted her to continue breastfeeding. I asked the midwife to check her and she said the stitches were healed and she was fine and she talked to her about the possibility of giving one bottle at night if she absolutely must ... the result of that was C banned the midwife from the flat - again! This was a frequent occurrence.

The next day she told me she had given a bottle of formula during the night. And then proudly produced a huge amount of expressed breast milk in a bottle! The reason for this was that we were going to the local Baby Café for the first time and she said she was not under any circumstances going to breastfeed there!

After that the bottles seemed to be forgotten about. I never knew where I was with her.

I saw her most days and spoke to her several times a day on the phone at her insistence. About three weeks after the birth while I was visiting her she asked if I could stay with her for a long time and look after her because I was more "fun" than the other people she dealt with. She also hinted that she was having sex again and when I reminded her about contraception she told me she was "trying for another baby"!

The next day she complained about the baby being unsettled although he seemed fine and a couple of days after that she rang to say that he had wanted two bottles one after the other and that she didn't want to breastfeed any more. When I went round I checked the formula tin and found it two thirds empty. I really didn't know how much she was breastfeeding although that morning we went to Baby Café again and she breast fed in front of everyone! Having complained bitterly about going to Baby Café she then didn't want to go home as she said it was pointless going there just for a couple of hours and she wanted to stay all day. Then, when we got home she said she didn't want to go again!

A few days later I got a call from her panicking that the baby had been sick. The health visitor also rang me with some concerns that she had. When I got round there, he was fine but I found she had put a pillow under him in the Moses basket because she "wanted him to be comfortable." I suggested she remove it and explained why and said that the midwife would say the same thing. Her reply was that she will never let her in the flat again and that the baby would not "smothercate!" The next day the midwife did visit and was let in and reiterated what I had said about the pillow. They had a huge row and she was thrown out again! C rang me and shouted at me and said I was banned too. Later she sent me a text saying she was sorry. However, later her boyfriend rang and apologised for her behaviour and said he was leaving her as he could not cope with her anymore and that he "might do something bad." He seemed unable to understand that she has learning difficulties and can't really help herself. At one point she said to me "just because I have learning difficulties doesn't mean I'm stupid." I think he thought she was being difficult for the sake of it.

At this point I told the midwife that I felt out of my depth as a doula. She agreed we should pass her onto someone with specialist knowledge of how to work with her.

The next day - my last day with her, I took her to the dentist where she announced at the top of her voice in the waiting room that she had had unprotected sex the night before and hoped she was pregnant. Three weeks after having a third degree tear ....

Working with C was a roller coaster ride for me as a doula. I actually grew very fond of her but she drove me crazy. She was a liability to take anywhere as she said loudly exactly what she thought of everyone and everything she saw. And it was impossible to reason with her. Much of my role felt like damage limitation. I have had no training in working with someone with special needs as such. All I could draw on was my considerable life experience and hope for the best. I had concerns for the safety of the baby in her hands although I know she loved him. She would often say things like "He is doing my head in. I've already fed him today. I'm not doing it again." But despite this he thrived.

When it was decided that I should withdraw from her, I found it impossible to explain to her that I would not be seeing her again. She would not accept it and in the end I had to resort to just not answering her calls. I felt bad about that but it was all I could do and in the end she stopped calling me. I met her in the street a few months later and she was delighted to see me and seemed well and happy."

Contributed by Lesley Hilton, birth and postnatal doula, Leeds area

3. Doula Journeys

Becoming a doula

"It is difficult to pinpoint when my doula journey began.
Was it:

- *destiny - with my mother passionate about birth, its miracle and the privilege we have as women to experience it?*

- *the birth of my eldest and the realisation that I truly shared these feelings?*

- *when I was overwhelmed by the difference a doula's support made to my final birth experience?*

- *when I picked up the phone to enquire about a doula course and found that it felt so "right"?*

Having spent 12 years as an at-home mum, a huge privilege in itself, I felt that I wanted to do something to fill the few available hours in my day now that the children were all at school. Since any work would increase the pressures of having a family and take me away from them, I had to feel passionate about what I was doing.

Supporting women and couples on their birthing and parenting journey as a birth and postnatal doula appeared interesting, would require learning new skills, meant I could decide how much or little I worked (or so I thought), and meant I could work around the children – except of course for a birth. I didn't appreciate at this stage how absorbed I would become, how much it would demand of me on both a physical and emotional level and most importantly how fulfilled I would feel doing it.

Turning to Google, I discovered the doula network Doula UK which appeared to provide me with the framework, training, support and invaluable friendship I would need as I took my first steps on my doula journey. I was also fortunate to know a couple of working doulas: I, who had been such a support to me as I birthed my daughter and L, a mother in one of my son's classes. In true doula fashion, they were warm, supportive and enthusiastic in making suggestions (not giving advice!) in how I should proceed. I also spoke with Doula UK's training co-ordinator who helped me clarify which course may best suit me.

I was pointed towards Maddie and Linda, the course leaders of Developing Doulas, who provided me with insight, wisdom, guidance and practical tips on how to be a doula. This is very difficult to do as so much is just about who you are, but they provided a fantastic framework and support. Within months I had read much, completed assignments, enhanced old and learned new skills, met other trainees and doulas – and much more.

With a feeling of apprehension and pride, my doula certificate in hand, I contacted Bridget, my potential Doula UK Assessor Mentor. Anyone can call themselves a doula but my certificate and the recognition process I was embarking upon, was the key to being a Doula UK doula, something I very much wanted and am proud of.

Having found someone to "doula" me as I learned to doula, I set about the task of finding clients. I started to think about my own personal doula philosophy, prepared a doulaography, I made business cards, thought about the wording in my contract, sorted out legalities, got some insurance and all the other jobs involved in starting a business. At the same time, I kept reading books and discovering websites which helped to increase my knowledge.

Surprisingly quickly, through a combination of other doulas recommending me and potential clients reading my doulaography, I found myself with 3 clients booked. Apparently a bonus of being a London doula.

One aspect of my training and ongoing work as a doula has been to constantly debrief my own birth experiences. This is such a valuable part of being a doula, although not always easy and often emotional, but we cannot support our clients unless we are as much at peace as possible with our own experiences.

Another privilege of being a doula is the opportunity to meet people. The exceptional women out there all with such varied backgrounds and different stories to tell but all sharing a passion for motherhood and birth. I find myself loving the way, from the first interview, the relationship develops with all the usual social reservations to the complete openness at the birth, where we truly see our clients both vulnerable but strong, to the closeness and mutual gratefulness afterwards.

I won't pretend that it has all been easy and stress free, but is anything worth doing ever easy? I now spend hours after my children have gone to bed, researching topics on the internet, reading and learning from forums (DUK and ukmidwifery), doing household jobs that I haven't done earlier as I have been with clients, talking to other doulas on the phone. I need to do work on setting boundaries and pacing myself, but I find it so interesting and can't resist supporting anyone who contacts me.

On the other hand, a pleasant surprise is how easy I have found being on call and needing to leave home at short notice. Even with one birth being a long drawn out induction during half-term, and another being 4 hours from first call to delivery. I prepare my clients to call me and keep me informed of any developments, I keep a freezer with easy meals even my husband can manage, a strong local network of friends and my mother, who is really fabulous at stepping in for me, to look after the kids.

I have found that I am able to stay up all night, love being needed by people and aiming to fulfil this need, am enjoying the company of likeminded women and so much more. One of the reasons I chose this job was also for my daughter who, being the only girl and last child, will never see me pregnant or be around babies and that, somehow from seeing what I do and hearing about it, she can see how birth and motherhood are not something to fear but something that is a privilege of womanhood, to be enjoyed and empowered by.

It is hard to put into words how much I love being a doula and how important I feel it is, for women to have unconditional support. So often we beat ourselves up as women or mothers and it is important to put this aside for birth, a doula's support can enable that to happen."

Contributed by Debra Virchis, doula, London

From doula to midwife

"More and more, I reflect on why being 'with woman' is so important to me, why I am following a path now to midwifery, and I really think (that) for me, it's about preserving this collective, semi-conscious wisdom of gentle birth. How is it that when we experience gentle birth -- when we feel, for the first time, a baby's head moving down through our body -- that it's a feeling which is simultaneously new, and familiar? We know, as a society, how to birth our babies, but so many of us have forgotten it or been forced to deny it because of unkind 'care' givers or negative cultural messages. We know this and we must preserve it, pass it down to other women, to our daughters, to anyone who'll listen. This, I think, is what doulas are passionate about, and if it means that we end up crossing that river into midwifery, then so be it. Did I tell you about the birth last year where my woman ended up giving birth standing up in the rain just outside the entrance to the (maternity unit) at 5 o'clock in the morning? How I had to catch the baby because her husband had disappeared into the hospital in search of a midwife and she was too involved in the moment to reach down and do it herself? I am clear that, as a doula, I would never presume to catch a baby 'on purpose', but when I reached under her dress and felt that slippery face and little nose just coming through, it was like I'd done that and felt that a million times before. (Fortunately the midwives came a split second after the baby was actually born, and everything was fine, and mum was thrilled with the way it all happened.) How is it that this knowledge is there, in our bones?"

Contributed by Leah Hazard, doula/student midwife, Glasgow

REFERENCES

Frontispiece

1. Kitzinger, S. Ch 12 Moving Forward, The Listening Experience. *Birth Crisis*. London: Routledge, Taylor & Francis Group, 2006, p.151

PART 1 – GRASSROOTS
1. Origins of the doula

1. Sterrenberg, M. What is a doula and why birthing women need them. It's a Small World, 2006 [Online] Available from: http://www.doulas.co.za/home [Accessed 4th October 2010]
2. Thiele, A. *Ancient Egyptian Midwifery and Childbirth,* 2002. [Online] Available from: http://www.mnsu.edu/emuseum/prehistory/egypt/dailylife/midwifery.htm [Accessed 4th October 2010]
3. Brucker, M. *The Birth of Midwifery*. [Online] Available from: http://www3.utsouthwestern.edu/midwifery/mdwfhistory.html [Accessed 4th October 2010]
4. BirthChoiceUK *Research about Support during Childbirth* [Online] Available from: http://www.birthchoiceuk.com/SupportResearch.htm [Accessed 4th October 2010]
5. MIDIRS. Support in Labour for Women. *Informed Choice Leaflet 1,* 2008. [Online] Available from: http://www.infochoice.org/ic/ic.nsf/RevLeaflets?OpenForm [Accessed 4th October 2010]
6. Definition of a midwife. Answers.com [Online] Available from: http://www.answers.com/topic/midwife [Accessed 4th October 2010]
7. Towler, J. & Bramall, J. *Midwives in History and Society.* London: Croom Helm, 1986.
8. *The Holy Bible,* Old Testament, Book of Genesis Ch 35, Verse 17
9. Studylight.org *The Old Testament Hebrew Lexicon* 2010 [Online] Available from: http://www.studylight.org/lex/heb/view.cgi?number=03205 [Accessed 4th October 2010]
10. Parsons, M. *Childbirth and Children in Ancient Egypt,* 2002. [Online] Available from: http://www.touregypt.net/featurestories/mothers.htm [Accessed 4th October 2010]
11. French, V. Midwives and Maternity care in the Roman World, Rescuing Creusa: New Methodological Approaches to Women in Antiquity. New

Series, *Helios*, 1986, 13(2), pp.69-84 [Online] Available from: http://www.indiana.edu/~ancmed/midwife.HTM [Accessed 4th October 2010]

12. Thomas, SS. Early modern midwifery: splitting the profession, connecting the history. The Free Library, *Journal of Social History*, 2009. [Online] Available from: http://www.thefreelibrary.com/Early+modern+midwifery%3a+splitting+the+profession%2c+connecting+the...a0209577951 [Accessed 4th October 2010]

13. Fox, E. Midwifery in England and Wales before 1936: handywomen and doctors. *International History of Nursing Journal*, 1995, Autumn 1(2), pp.17-28 [Online] Available from: http://www.researchgate.net/publication/11732400_Midwifery_in_England_and_Wales_before_1936_handywomen_and_doctors [Accessed 4th October 2010]

14. Reid, L. *Scottish Midwives: Twentieth Century Voices*. Dunfermline: Black Devon Books, 2008.

15. Rooks, J. & Mahan, CS. *Midwifery and Childbirth in America*. Philadelphia: Temple University Press, 1997.

16. Robilliard, G. *Accoucheur - City Council – Midwives - Mothers: Choosing midwives in early modern Leipzig* presented at the Civil Society and Public Service: Early Modern Europe, Leiden, Netherlands, 2007, Dec 30 [Online] Available from: http://www.let.leidenuniv.nl/pdf/geschiedenis/civil/Robbillard.pdf [Accessed 4th October 2010]

17. De Lourdes Verderese, M. & Turnbull, L. *A Traditional Birth Attendant in Maternal and Child Health and Family Planning: a guide to her training and utilization*. Geneva: World Health Organisation, 1975.

18. Klaus, MH., Kennell, JH. & Klaus, P. *The Doula Book*. Cambridge, MA: Perseus Publishing, 2002.

19. *Stone relief from Isola Dell' Sacra*, Ostia, 1st century CE [Online] Available from: http://www.hsl.virginia.edu/historical/artifacts/antiqua/women.cfm [Accessed 4th October 2010]

20. *A midwife and an assistant stand by at the birth of twins*, miniature from Chururgia, Gerard of Cremona, 12th century, Codex Series Nova 2641, fol 41 r. Osterreichische Nationalbibliothek, Vienna [Online] Available from: http://mw.mcmaster.ca/scriptorium/images/3008w-Childbirth.html [Accessed 4th October 2010]

21. *Birth of the Virgin*, Venetian School, c. 1480 [Online] Available from: http://www.delmars.com/cats/gallery/catsart2.htm [Accessed 1st March 2010]

22. *A woman giving birth on a birth chair* Eucharius Rößlin, *Der Swangern frawen vnd hebamme(n) roszgarte(n)* Ch 4 Hagenau: Gran 1515 [Online] Available from: http://en.wikipedia.org/wiki/File:Eucharius_R%C3%B6%C3%9Flin_Rosgarten_Childbirth.jpg [Accessed 4th October 2010]

23. Sterrenberg, M. (Op.cit.), 2006

24. Wiesner-Hanks, ME. Ordinance Regulating Midwives, Germany 1522 (pdf) Ch 8 Individuals in Society 1600-1789. 1. Primary Sources. 15. *Early Modern Europe 1450-1789*. Cambridge: Cambridge University Press 2006. [Online] Available from: http://www.cambridge.org/catalogue/catalogue.asp?isbn=9780521005210&resISBN13=9780521808941&parent=3072&ss=res#resource [Accessed 4th October 2010]

25. Dictionary.com [Online] Available from: http://dictionary.reference.com/browse/gossip [Accessed 4th October 2010]

26. Raphael D. *The Tender Gift: Breastfeeding*. Englewood Cliffs, New Jersey: Prentice-Hall, 1973

27. Raphael, D. Interview with Reiko Kishi, *Breastfeeding and Doula Support*. Child Research Net, 2005 [Online] Available from: http://www.childresearch.net/SCIENCE/DIALOGS/2007/index.html [Accessed 4th October 2010]

28. Olivier, J. Sesotho Online [Online] Available from: www.sesotho.web.za/dipolelo.htm [Accessed 4th October 2010]

29. Stockton, A. Prenatal Support and Preparation for Birth – the Doula's Role *The Practising Midwife*, May, 2010, pp.26-27&30

30. Klaus, M., Kennell, J., Klaus, P. et al. DONA International Founders: *Mothering the Mother*. [Online] Available from: www.dona.org/aboutus/founders.php [Accessed 4th October 2010]

31. Sosa, R., Kennell, JH., Klaus, MH. et al. The effect of a supportive companion on perinatal problems, length of labor, and mother-infant interaction. *New England Journal of Medicine*, 1980, 303, pp.597-600

32. Klaus, MH., Kennell, JH., Robertson, SS. et al.. Effects of social support during parturition on maternal and infant morbidity. *British Medical Journal*, 1986, 293, pp.585-587

33. Klaus, MH., Kennell, JH. & Klaus, P. (Op.cit.), 2002

34. DONA *Vision and Mission Statement* [Online] Available from: www.dona.org/aboutus/mission.php [Accessed 4th October 2010]

35. Ne'eman Staff, Y. Hansy Josovic Activists from Stamford Hill Go to Venice, *Dei'ah veDibur Information & Insight,* 9th August 2006 [Online] Available from: http://chareidi.shemayisrael.com/archives5766/eikev/ahjmcekv66.htm [Accessed 4th October 2010]

36. Parkinson, D. Director, Birth Companions. Personal telephone communication with Adela Stockton, 2009

37. Birtles, J. Director, British Doulas. Personal telephone communication with Adela Stockton, 2009

38. Lammers, L. Doula Course Facilitator, Paramana. Personal telephone communication with Adela Stockton, 2009

39. Lewin, H. *Doula UK - beginnings.* Personal email to Adela Stockton, 28th May 2010

40. Doula UK. *Minutes of the First Meeting of The Independent Doula Association* 10th February, 2001 [Online] Available from: http://www.doula.org.uk/content/duk/members/Previous Meetings Minutes.asp [Accessed 4th October 2010]

41. Lammers, L. (Op.cit.) 2009

2. 21st century doulas

1. Quinn, L. Course Leader, Developing Doulas. Personal telephone communication with Adela Stockton, 16th March 2010

2. Klaus et al., 2002; Rosen, 2004; Scott, Berkowitz, & Klaus, 1999 In: Ballen, LE. & Fulcher, AJ. Nurses and Doulas: Complementary Roles to Provide Optimal Maternity Care. *Journal of Obstetric, Gynecologic and Neonatal Nursing,* March/April 2006, Volume 35(2), pp.304–311

3. Baker, B. *Grandmothers of the doula community outside US.* Personal email to: Adela Stockton 17th March 2010

4. Baker, B. (Op.cit.), 2010

5. Hodnett, ED., Gates, S., Hofmeyr, GJ. et al. Continuous support for women during childbirth (Cochrane Review) IN: *The Cochrane Library,* Issue 2, Chichester, UK: John Wiley & Sons Ltd., 2003.

6. McGrath, Susan K. & Kennell, John H. A Randomized Controlled Trial of Continuous Labor Support for Middle-Class Couples: Effect on Cesarean Delivery Rates. *Birth,* 2008, 35(2), pp.92-97

7. Goldbert, J. Postpartum depression: bridging the gap between medicalised birth and social support. *International Journal of Childbirth Education,* 2002, 17(4), pp.11-17

8. Langer, A., Campero, L., Garcia, C. et al. Effects of psychosocial support during labour and childbirth on breastfeeding, medical interventions and mothers' wellbeing in a Mexican public hospital: a randomised clinical trial. *British Journal of Obstetrics and Gynaecology*, 1998, 105(10), pp.1056-63

9. Berg M & Terstad A. Swedish women's experiences of doula support during childbirth *Midwifery*, 2006, 22, pp.330-338

10. Kitzinger, S. *UK 'doula movement'*. Personal email to: Adela Stockton, 30th April, 2009

11. Odent M. Ch 15 The Future of the Midwifery-Obstetrics Relationship. *The Farmer and the Obstetrician*. London: Free Association Books, 2002, p.123

12. Buckley S. *Gentle Birth, Gentle Mothering* (2nd ed). Celestial Arts: Berkeley, California, 2009

13. Quinn, L. (Op.cit.), 2010

14. Birth Consultancy Mindful Doulas Course *Philosophy* [Online] Available from: http://www.adelastockton.co.uk/content/birth-consultancy-mindful-doulas-course [Accessed 4th October 2010]

15. McMahon, M. Course Leader, Developing Doulas. Personal telephone communication with Adela Stockton. 2009

16. Quinn, L. (Op.cit.), 2010

17. wysewomen *Workshops* [Online] Available from: http://sites.google.com/site/wysewomen/home/workshops [Accessed 4th October 2010]

3. UK 'brand' of doula

1. Bogossian, F. *The Bob and June Prickett Churchill Fellowship; to examine the scope of practice, education and regulation of doulas (trained birth companions)*. The Winston Churchill Memorial Trust of Australia, Churchill Fellow Report 2006 f.bogossian@uq.edu.au

2. Goedkoop, V. *MIDIRS Midwifery Digest*, June 2009, 19(2), pp.217-218

3. Meyer, BA., Arnold, JA. & Pascali-Bonaro, D. Social Support by Doulas during Labor and the Early Postpartum Period. *Hospital Physician*, September 2001 pp.57-65 [Online] Available from: http://www.turner-white.com/hp/hp03_past2001.htm#september [Accessed 4th October 2010]

4. Simkin, P. *UK doulas*. Personal email to: Adela Stockton, 21st September, 2007

5. Hazard, L. *Updated chapters.* Personal email to: Adela Stockton, 13th May 2010

6. Developing Doulas. *Mission Statement.* [Online] Available from: http://www.developingdoulas.co.uk/?q=content/mission-statement [Accessed 4th October 2010]

7. Birthing Wisdom. *Training.* [Online] Available from: http://www.birthingwisdom.co.uk/training/training.html [Accessed 4th October 2010]

8. Holistic Birth Trust Foundation. *Homepage.* [Online] Available from: http://www.holisticbirthtrust.org [Accessed 4th October 2010]

9. Conscious Birthing. *Conscious Birthing Ethos.* [Online] Available from: http://www.consciousbirthing.co.uk [Accessed 4th October 2010]

10. Nurturing Birth. *Doula training.* [Online] Available from: http://www.nurturingbirth.co.uk/doula_courses.html [Accessed 4th October 2010]

11. Doula Consultancy Services. *Doula Training University Benefits.* [Online] Available from: http://findadoula.org.uk/doulatrainingaccreditedbymiddlesexuniversity/id50.html [Accessed 4th October 2010]

12. Ryan, N. NCT Media Relations Manager. *Press enquiry: NCT Birth Companions course.* Personal email to: Adela Stockton, 6th October 2010

13. Expectancy, Complementary Therapies Consultancy. PROSPECTUS: *Maternity Support Therapist programme, Certificate in Maternity Complementary Therapies* [Online] Available from: http://www.expectancy.co.uk/courses.php [Accessed 4th October 2010]

14. Tiran, D. *Maternity Support Therapist programme.* Personal email to: Adela Stockton, 16th April 2010

15. Houser, P. Speech - *Doulas: Serving Humanity,* Doula UK Doula of the Year Awards Ceremony, London with Ricki Lake. 7th Oct 2009 [Online] Available from: http://www.mybestbirth.com/profiles/blog/show?id=3120006%3ABlogPost%3A36436&commentId=3120006%3AComment%3A37797 [Accessed 4th October 2010]

16. International Confederation of Midwives. *Essential Competencies for Basic Midwifery Practice* 2002. [Online] Available (PDF) from: http://www.internationalmidwives.org/Regulation/tabid/347/Default.aspx [Accessed 4th October 2010]

17. Bogossian, F. (Op.cit.), 2006

18. Nursing & Midwifery Council. *Advice sheet: Free birthing* March, 2008. [Online] Available from: http://www.nmc-uk.org/Nurses-and-midwives/Advice-by-topic/A/Advice/Free-birthing/ [Accessed 4th October 2010]

19. Edwards, NP. *Birthing Autonomy – Women's Experiences of Planning Home Births.* London: Routledge, Taylor & Francis Group, 2005 p.95

20. Chakladar, A. Encounter with a doula: is the NHS failing mothers? *BMJ* 2009, 339(7733), p.1316

21. Doula UK. *Become a doula,* 2009. [Online] Available from: http://www.doula.org.uk/content/duk/become/How_to_become_a_Doula.asp [Accessed 4th October 2010]

22. Doula UK. *Philosophy,* 2009. [Online] Available from: http://www.doula.org.uk/content/duk/doulauk/Philosophy.asp [Accessed 4th October 2010]

23. Doula UK. *Code of Conduct,* 2009. [Online] Available from: http://www.doula.org.uk/content/duk/doulauk/Code_of_Conduct.asp [Accessed 4th October 2010]

24. Birtles, J. (Op.cit.), 2009

25. Doula UK. *Hardship Fund,* 2009. [Online] Available from: http://www.doula.org.uk/content/duk/doulauk/Hardship_Fund.asp [Accessed 4th October 2010]

26. Goodwin Volunteer Doula Project. *Our Aims for the Project,* 2008. [Online] Available from: http://www.goodwindoulas.org/aims+and+objectives [Accessed 4th October 2010]

27. Birth Companions. *How we work,* 2009. [Online] Available from: http://www.birthcompanions.org.uk/howwework.html [Accessed 4th October 2010]

28. Scottish Doula Network. *Ethical Statement,* 2008. [Online] Available from: http://www.scottishdoulanetwork.co.uk/2.html [Accessed 4th October 2010]

4. The wider doula community

1. Goodall, N. Doula & Workshop facilitator, Wysewomen. *Essence of a doula.* Personal email to: Adela Stockton, 24th September 2010

2. l'association Doulas de France. *The European Doula Guide.* First presented at 5th French Doulas Convention, May 2007. Available from: http://www.doulas.info/cahier2.php [Accessed 4th October 2010]

3. Chalmers, L. *Australian Doulas*. Personal email to: Adela Stockton, 17th December 2009

4. Sterrenberg, M. (Op.cit) 2006

5. Childbirth International *Doulas Internationally* 2008 [Online] Available from: http://www.childbirthinternational.com/information/international. htm [Accessed 4th October 2010]

6. Dupin, V. Personal telephone conversation with Adela Stockton, 2009

7. Castro C. *Portuguese doula*. Personal email to Adela Stockton, 13th April 2010

8. Stockton, A. Author's personal experience of Da-a-luz (holistic pregnancy centre), Orgiva, Spain. October 2010

9. Dupin, V. (Op.cit.), 2009

10. Dupin, V. Personal email to Adela Stockton, 23rd April 2010

11. doula.nl. *English page*. [Online] Available from: http://www.doula.nl/ [Accessed 4th October 2010]

12. Walker, J. *Doulas in your country (Netherlands)*. Personal email to Adela Stockton, 14th April 2010

13. van Tuyl, T. & Bruyn S. *De Doula, emotionele ondersteuning bij de bevalling*, 2006. Available to order from: http://www.doula.nl/ Doula-boekenhoek page. [Accessed 4th October 2010]

14. Walker, J. (Op.cit.), 2010

15. Stockton, A. Author's personal experience of maternity hospital, Setubal, Portugal.

16. Castro C. (Op.cit.), 2010

17. l'association Doulas de France (Op.cit.), 2007

18. doulasbarcelona *Who we are* [Online] Available from: http:// doulasbarcelona.org/en/node/53 [Accessed 4th October 2010]

19. Schöne, M. *Doulas in your country (Germany)*. Personal email to Adela Stockton, 17th March 2010

20. Wierzba-Bloedorn, K. *Doulas Germany*. Personal email to: Adela Stockton, 23rd March 2010

21. Mindful Doulas, author's own doula course records, 2010

22. Developing Doulas. Personal email to: Adela Stockton

23. Nurturing Birth. *Homepage,* 2010 [Online] Available from: http://www. nurturingbirth.co.uk [Accessed 4th October 2010]

24. Childbirth International, (Op.cit.), 2008

25. ODIS – Organisation for doulas and childbirth educators in Scandinavia *Information in English* [Online] Available from: http://www.doula.nu/english.php [Accessed 4th October 2010]

26. Berg, M. & Terstad, A. (Op.cit.), 2006

27. Lundgren, I. Swedish women's experiences of doula support during childbirth. *Midwifery* April 2010, Vol 26(2), pp.173-180

28. l'association Doulas de France (Op.cit.), 2007

29. Birchler-Stratmann, M., Brunner, R., Derman-L, Anke. & Strehler-Heubeck, B. *History of the European Doula Network-Movement.* Position Report towards a European Doula Network, Feusisberg, Switzerland, 17th/18th April 2009. Available via l'association Doulas de France http://www.doulas.info/contact.php [Accessed 4th October 2010]

30. Birchler-Stratmann, M., Brunner, R., Soumah, AL., Strehler-Heubeck, B., Singer, A. & Lanfranchi, S. *Revised Document for a European Doula Network,* Munich, Germany 20th/21st March 2010

31. Rye, V. *Doulas in New Zealand.* Personal email to: Adela Stockton, 2008

32. Chalmers, L. (Op.cit.), 2009

33. Nurturing Birth, (Op.cit.), 2010

34. Mindful Doulas, (Op.cit.), 2010

35. Developing Doulas, (Op.cit.), 2010

36. Sterrenberg, M. *About the Village Author and Facilitator* [Online] Available from: http://www.doulas.co.za/home/about-the-village-doula-training [Accessed 4th October 2010]

37. Doula Organisation of South Africa *Vision and Mission* [Online] Available from: http://doula.org.za/vision-and-mission/ [Accessed 4th October 2010]

38. Doula Organisation of South Africa *Homepage* [Online] Available from: http://doula.org.za [Accessed 4th October 2010]

39. Childbirth International, (Op.cit.), 2008

40. NHS Maternity Statistics, England: 2007-08, April 2009 [Online] Available from: http://www.ic.nhs.uk/statistics-and-data-collections/hospital-care/maternity/nhs-maternity-statistics-england:-2007-08 [Accessed 4th October 2010]

41. Births & Babies, Mode of Delivery: 1976-2008, Information Services Division Scotland, September 2009 [Online] Available from: http://www.isdscotland.org/isd/1612.html [Accessed 4th October 2010]

42. Hamilton, BE., Martin, AM. & Ventura SJ. Births: Preliminary Data for 2007 *National Vital Statistics Reports* Vol 57(12), March 18th 2009. [Online] Available (PDF) from: http://www.theunnecesarean.com/blog/2009/3/18/c-section-rate-rises-2007-us-cesarean-rate-hit-318-percent.html [Accessed 4th October 2010]

43. World Health Organization. Appropriate technology for birth. *Lancet* 1985, 2, pp.436-7

44. Betran, AP., Merialdi, M., Lauer, JA. et al. Rates of caesarean section: analysis of global, regional and national estimates. *Paediatric & Perinatal Epidemiology* 2007, 21, pp.98–113 **IN** Barbieri, RL. OBC Management, *Editorial: How will we know it when we've got the right cesarean rate?* June 2008, 20(6), pp.13-15 [Online] Available from: http://www.obgmanagement.com/article_pages.asp?AID=6295&UID=#bib1 [Accessed 4th October 2010]

45. Festin, MR., Laopaiboon, M., Pattanittum, P. et al. & The SEA-ORCHID Study Group. Caesarean section in four South East Asian countries: reasons for, rates, associated care practices and health outcomes *BMC* Pregnancy Childbirth, May 2009, 9, p.17 [Online] Available from: http://www.ncbi.nlm.nih.gov/pmc/articles/PMC2695422/ [Accessed 4th October 2010]

46. Béhague, DP., Victora, CG. & Barros, FC. Consumer demand for caesarean sections in Brazil: informed decision-making, patient choice, or social inequality? *BMJ* 2002, 324, p.942

Part 2 - GUARDIANS OF GENTLE BIRTH?
1. Birth space, Safe place: role of the birth doula

1. Walker, J. Doula in Netherlands, *Facebook Wall, Information Box* 2010 [Online] Available from: http://www.facebook.com/people/Adela-Stockton/1373529938#!/jenniferannwalker?v=wall [Accessed 4th October 2010]

2. Hodnett, ED., Gates, S., Hofmeyr, GJ. & Sakala, C. Continuous support for women during childbirth. *Cochrane Database of Systematic Reviews* 2007, Issue 3

3. Klaus MH, Kennell JH, Robertson SS, Sosa R. Effects of social support during parturition on maternal and infant morbidity. *British Medical Journal* 1986, 293:585–587

4. Khreisheh, R. Support in the first stage of labour from a female relative: the first step in improving the quality of maternity services. *Midwifery* 2009 (Article in Press)

5. Berg, M. & Terstad, A. (Op.cit.), 2006

6. Lundgren, I. (Op.cit.), 2010

7. McGrath, SK. & Kennel, JH. A Randomized Controlled Trial of Continuous Labor Support for Middle-Class Couples: Effect on Cesarean Delivery Rates. *Birth* 2008, 35(2), pp.92-97

8. Koumouitzes-Douvia, J. & Carr, CA. Women's Perceptions of their Doula Support. *Journal of Perinatal Education* 2006, 15(4), pp.34-40 [Online] Available (PDF) from: http://www.ncbi.nlm.nih.gov/pmc/articles/PMC1804309/#citeref12 [Accessed 4th October 2010]

9. Trueba, G., Contreras, C., Velazco, MT., Lara, EG. & Martínez, HB. Alternative Strategy to Decrease Cesarean Section: Support by Doulas During Labor. *Journal of Perinatal Education* Spring 2000, 9(2), pp.8-13

10. Klaus MH, Kennell JH, Robertson SS, Sosa R. (Op.cit.), 1986

11. Buckley, S. Undisturbed Birth – nature's hormonal blueprint for safety, ease and ecstasy. MIDIRS Midwifery Digest, June 2004, 14(2), pp.203-209

12. Buckley, S. What disturbs birth? MIDIRS Midwifery Digest, Sept 2004, 14(3), pp.353-359

13. Klaus, M., Kennel, J. & Klaus, P. (Op.cit.), 2002

14. Campbell, D. Men should 'stay away from childbirth' - leading obstetrician claims that women are more likely to have a host of problems if partners are at delivery. *The Observer*, Sunday 18th October, 2009

15. Gaskin, I.M. *Cheyenne's Amazing Labor* 20th February, 2004 [Online] Available from: http://www.inamay.com/?page_id=210 [Accessed 4th October 2010]

16. Birthing by Heart *Using a Rebozo for Foetal Positioning* [Online] Available from: http://www.birthingbyheart.com/doulas/rebozo-foetal-positioning/ [Accessed 4th October 2010]

17. Lammers, L. (Op.cit.), 2009

18. Nursing & Midwifery Council (Op.cit.), March 2008

19. Nursing & Midwifery Council Op.cit.), March 2008

20. Puig, G. & Sguassero, Y. Early skin-to-skin contact for mothers and their healthy newborn infants: RHL commentary (last revised: 9 November 2007). *The WHO Reproductive Health Library*; Geneva: World Health

Organization. [Online] Available from: http://apps.who.int/rhl/newborn/ gpcom/en/ [Accessed 4th October 2010]

21. Newman, J. Breastfeeding Online, Handout 1a: "Skin to Skin Contact", *The importance of skin to skin contact* Jan 2005 [Online] Available (as PDF) from: http://www.breastfeedingonline.com/newman.shtml [Accessed 4th October 2010]

22. Mickwitz, D. Doula. Personal conversation with Adela Stockton, 2009.

2. Continuum parenting: role of the postnatal doula

1. Gerhardt, S. *Why love Matters: how affection shapes a baby's brain.* Routledge: London 2004 p.57

2. Campbell, D., Scott, KD., Klaus, MH. & Falk, M. Female Relatives or Friends Trained as Labor Doulas: Outcomes at 6 to 8 Weeks Postpartum. *Birth* Sept 2007, Vol 34(3), pp.220–227

3. Mottl-Santiago, J., Walker, C., Ewan, J., Vragovic, O., Winder, S. & Stubblefield, P. A hospital-based doula program and childbirth outcomes in an urban, multicultural setting. *Maternal and Child Health Journal* May 2008, Vol 12(3), pp.372-377

4. Langer, A., Campero, L., Garcia, C. & Reynoso, S. Effects of psychosocial support during labour and childbirth on breastfeeding, medical interventions, and mothers' wellbeing in a Mexican public hospital: a randomised clinical trial. *British Journal of Obstetrics & Gynaecology* Oct 1998, 105(10), pp.1056-63

5. McComish, JF. & Visger, JM. Domains of Postpartum Doula Care and Maternal Responsiveness and Competence. *Journal of Obstetric, Gynaecologic & Neonatal Nursing* Mar/Apr 2009, Vol 38(2), pp.148-156

6. Goldbort, J. Postpartum depression: Bridging the gap between medicalized birth and social support International. *Journal of Childbirth Education* Dec 2002

7. Gerhardt, S. (Op.cit) 2004

8. Liedloff, J. *The Continuum Concept: in search of happiness lost.* 5th Ed. Penguin Books: London 2004

9. Ford, G. *The New Contented Little Baby Book: the secret to calm and confident parenting.* Vermillion: London 2006

10. Kitzinger, S. *Birth Crisis.* Routledge: London 2006

11. Kitzinger, S. (Op.cit.) 2006

3. Doulaing: social support or return to traditional midwifery?

1. Parvati Baker, J. *Homepage,* 2005 [Online] Available from: http://birthkeeper.org/ [Accessed 4th October 2010]
2. Brooks, V. *TM in Spain.* Personal email to Adela Stockton, 7th October 2009
3. Pollack Ellam, T. Home Birth Bullying. *AIMS Journal,* 2010 Vol 22(1), pp.22-23
4. Mander, R., Murphy-Lawless, J. & Edwards, N. Reflecting on good birthing: an innovative approach to culture change. Part 2. *MIDIRS Midwifery Digest,* March 2010 Vol 20(1), pp.25-29
5. Beech, B. Midwifery – who cares what women want? *AIMS Journal,* 2010 Vol 22(1), pp.3-4
6. Nicoll, A & Winters, P. Community Maternity Units – what can they do? *Paper for North of Scotland Maternity Services Framework Group/NES,* Nairn, 15th-16th February 2006 [Online] Available from: http://www.birthinangus.org.uk/index/nairn [Accessed 4th October 2010]
7. Save the Albany website. *Facts & Figures.* [Online] Available from: http://www.savethealbany.org.uk/ALBANY/Welcome.html [Accessed 4th October 2010]
8. Edwards, N. Reclaiming Birth Rally. *AIMS Journal,* 2010 Vol 22(1), p.4
9. Independent Midwives UK website. *Our Campaign.* [Online] Available from: http://www.independentmidwives.org.uk/?node=8766 [Accessed 4th October 2010]
10. Schaefer, P. Homebirth midwife. Personal telephone conversation with Adela Stockton, 26th April 2010
11. Home births in Hungary: Difficult delivery – The pioneer of home births in Hungary faces jail. *The Economist,* 11th March 2010 [Online] Available from: http://www.economist.com/node/15671546?story_id=15671546&source=hptextfeature [Accessed 4th October 2010]
12. Ockwell-Smith, S. My First 999 Experience. *Doulaing - Doula UK Newsletter,* Spring 2010 Issue 17, pp.7-8 Available (PDF) from: http://www.doula.org.uk/content/duk/members/Newsletters_Articles.asp [Accessed 4th October 2010]
13. Higgins, H. A Slightly Tricky Call. *Doulaing – Doula UK Newsletter,* Spring 2010 Issue 17, pp.9-11 Available (PDF) from: http://www.doula.org.uk/content/duk/members/Newsletters_Articles.asp [Accessed 4th October 2010]

14. Groskop, V. Going it alone. *The Guardian*, Wednesday 9th May 2007 [Online] Available from: http://www.guardian.co.uk/society/2007/may/09/health.medicineandhealth [Accessed 4th October 2010]

15. Kellum, R. *The Birthrite of Samuel Rune*, 2002 [Online] Available from: http://rachyllgyne.tripod.com/thebirthriteofsamuelrune/id1.html [Accessed 4th October 2010]

16. Gaskin, IM. *Spiritual Midwifery* (3rd ed.) The Book Publishing Company: Tennesee, 1990

17. Da-a-luz website. *About us*, 2010 [Online] Available from: http://www.da-a-luz.co.uk/aboutus.php [Accessed 4th October 2010]

18. Parvati Baker, J. (Op.cit) 2005

PART 3 – DOULA TALES

1. Houser, P. (Op.cit) 2009

FURTHER RESOURCES [see also REFERENCES]

Pregnancy, Birth and Parenting: support & information

Active Birth Centre (UK) http://www.activebirthcentre.com

Association for Improvement in Maternity Services (AIMS) (UK) http://www.aims.org.uk, helpline@aims.org.uk or 0300-365-0663

Birth Crisis Network (UK) http://www.sheilakitzinger.com/BirthCrisis.htm

Da-a-luz Holistic Pregnancy Centre (Spain) http://www.da-a-luz.co.uk

Expectancy: Expectant Parents' Complementary Therapies Consultancy (UK) http://www.expectancy.co.uk/

Fathers-to-be (UK) http://www.fatherstobe.org

National Childbirth Trust (NCT) (UK) http://www.nctpregnancyandbabycare.com

Midwifery Today (Jan Tritten) (US) http://www.midwiferytoday.com

The Farm Midwifery Center, Tennessee (US) http://www.thefarmmidwives.org

Breastfeeding: support & information

Association of Breastfeeding Mothers (ABM) http://www.abm.me.uk
UK Helpline: 08444-122-949

Breastfeeding Network (BfN) http://www.breastfeedingnetwork.org.uk
UK Supporterline: 0300-100-0210

La Leche League
UK: http://www.laleche.org.uk Helpline: 0845-120-2918
International: http://www.llli.org

National Breastfeeding Helpline (UK): 0300 100 0212

National Childbirth Trust http://www.nctpregnancyandbabycare.com
UK Helpline: 0300-330-0771

Suzanne Colson on breastfeeding http://www.biologicalnurturing.com

Films

Doula! The Ultimate Birth Companion (Doula UK + Alto Films) http://www.doulafilm.com

Orgasmic Birth (Debra Bonaro Pascali) http://www.orgasmicbirth.com

The Business of Being Born (Ricky Lake) http://www.thebusinessofbeingborn.com

Doulas – Networks, Courses & Workshops

Australia

Australian Doulas http://www.australiandoulas.webs.com

Birthing Wisdom http://www.birthingwisdom.com.au

Directory of Childbirth Support Partners http://www.findadoula.com.au/index.php

Austria

Doulas in Austria http://www.doula.at/

Belgium

Association Francophone des Doulas de Belgique http://www.doulas.be/

Canada

Doula C.A.R.E. http://www.doulacare.ca

France

Doulas de France http://www.doulas.info/

Germany

Doulas in Deutschland http://www.doulas-in-deutschland.de/

http://www.doula-kristina.de/ (Kristina Wierzba-Bloedorn)

http://www.meine-doula.de/ (Melanie Shöne)

Hungary

Hungarian Doulas Association http://www.module.hu/ and http://www.doula.hu/

http://www.ashoka.org/fellow/2855 (Agnes Gereb)

Italy

http://www.doula.it/

Ireland

Doula Ireland http://www.doulaireland.com/

http://www.doulamayo.ie/(Claire Casby)

Netherlands

De Nederlands doula-site http://www.doula.nl/

http://www.doulaesther.nl/ (Esther Kokkelmans)

http://www.birthsupport.nl/ (Jennifer Walker)

http://www.theavantuyl.nl/ (Thea van Tuyl)

New Zealand

NurtureNZ http://www.nurturenz.com (Vida Rye)

Portugal

Doulas de Portugal http://doulasdeportugal.blogspot.com

Scandanavia

ODIS http://www.doula.nu/

Spain

Doulas en Espana http://www.doulas.es

Da-a-luz http://www.da-a-luz.co.uk

Switzerland

Doula-Geburtsbegleitung - Verband Doula CH & l'association Doula CH http://doula.ch/ (Regula Brunner & Michele Birchler)

South Africa

Doulas of South Africa http://www.doula.org.za

The Village http://www.doulas.co.za/ (Maria Sterrenberg)

WOMBS (Women Offering Mothers Birth Support) http://www.wombs.org.za/

United Kingdom

Birth Companions http://www.birthcompanions.org.uk

Birth Consultancy Mindful Doulas http://www.adelastockton.co.uk

Birthing Wisdom http://www.birthingwisdom.co.uk

British Doulas http://www.britishdoulas.co.uk

Conscious Birthing http://www.consciousbirthing.co.uk

Developing Doulas http://www.developingdoulas.co.uk

Doula UK http://www.doula.org.uk 0871-4333103

Goodwin Volunteer Doula Project http://www.goodwindoulas.org

Hansy Josovic Maternity Trust 020 8806 1571

Holistic Birth Trust http://www.holisticbirthtrust.org

Nurturing Birth http://www.nurturingbirth.co.uk

Paramanadoula http://www.paramanadoula.com

Scottish Doula Network http://www.scottishdoulanetwork.co.uk

Wysewomen http://sites.google.com/site/wysewomen/

USA

Doulas of North America International (DONA) http://www.dona.org/

http://www.pennysimkin.com

FURTHER READING [see also REFERENCES]

Books

Am I Allowed? B. Beech (2003) AIMS www.aims.org.uk

Birth Crisis S. Kitzinger (2005)

Birthing from Within P. England & R. Horowitz (Rev Ed 2007)

Birth Space, Safe Place: emotional wellbeing through pregnancy and birth A. Stockton (2009)

Continuum Concept: In search of happiness lost J. Leidloff (2004)

Fathers-to-be Handbook P. Houser (2008)

Gentle Birth, Gentle Mothering S. Buckley (Rev Ed 2009)

Ina May's Guide to Breastfeeding (2009), *Guide to Childbirth* (2003) or *Spiritual Midwifery* (3rd Ed) (1990) IM. Gaskin

Lotus Birth R. Shivam (Ed) (2000)

Primal Health: Understanding the Critical Period Between Conception and the First Birthday. M. Odent (Rev Ed 2007)

The Birth Partner: A Complete Guide to Childbirth for Dads, Doulas, and Other Labor Companions P. Simkin (2008) www.pennysimkin.com

The Doula Book: How a Trained Labor Companion can help you have a shorter, easier and healthier birth MH Klaus, PH Klaus & JH Kennell (2002)

The Father's Homebirth Handbook L. Hazard (2010)

Why Love Matters: How Affection Shapes a Baby's Brain S. Gerhardt (2004)

Journals

AIMS Journals www.aims.org.uk

Midwifery Today www.midwiferytoday.com

Juno magazine www.juno.com

Web articles

Cheyenne's Amazing Labor IM. Gaskin, 20th February, 2004 http://www.inamay. com/?page_id=210

Optimal Fetal Positioning www.spinningbabies.com

The Importance of Skin-to-Skin Contact (first feed) J. Newman (2005) www. breastfeedingonline.com

Articles by Adela Stockton at http://www.adelastockton.co.uk/content/published-articles

Various research/articles/press available at http://www.doula.org.uk/content/ duk/about/default.asp

Acknowledgments

I would like to thank all the women - daughters, sisters, mothers, grandmothers, doulas, midwives - and fathers who have so generously contributed, shared and helped nurture this book to fruition. I am especially grateful to Maddie McMahon for her care in editing my work, and with Leah Hazard, for their constructive feedback and encouragement throughout. My heartfelt thanks also to Vida Rye for her insights on the UK doula movement and to Penny Simkin for keeping me right on the differences between US and UK doulas. And finally, my deepest gratitude to Vanessa Brooks, Sue Paulding, Veronica Ramos, Paula Gallardo and all the other midwives and doulas involved with Da-a-luz, for their inspiration and trust in birth, and to my husband Matt Baker and my daughter Marly for their enduring love and support.

BY THE SAME AUTHOR

Birth Space, Safe Place: emotional wellbeing through pregnancy and birth
(Findhorn Press, 2009)